DESIGN FOR NEED

The Social Contribution of Design

DESIGN FOR NEED

The Social Contribution of Design

An anthology of papers presented to the
Symposium at the Royal College of Art, London, April 1976

Edited by
JULIAN BICKNELL
LIZ McQUISTON
The Royal College of Art

Published for ICSID by
PERGAMON PRESS
OXFORD · NEW YORK · TORONTO · SYDNEY · PARIS · FRANKFURT

U.K. *1977*   Pergamon Press Ltd., Headington Hill Hall,
               Oxford OX3 0BW, England

U.S.A.   Pergamon Press Inc., Maxwell House, Fairview Park,
               Elmsford, New York 10523, U.S.A.

CANADA   Pergamon of Canada Ltd., 75 The East Mall,
               Toronto, Ontario, Canada

AUSTRALIA   Pergamon Press (Aust.) Pty. Ltd., 19a Boundary Street,
               Rushcutters Bay, N.S.W. 2011, Australia

FRANCE   Pergamon Press SARL, 24 rue des Ecoles,
               75240 Paris, Cedex 05, France

WEST GERMANY   Pergamon Press GmbH, 6242 Kronberg-Taunus,
               Pferdstrasse 1, Frankfurt-am-Main, West Germany

This Compilation ©ICSID 1977

Library of Congress Cataloging in Publication Data

Main entry under title:
Design for need.

1. Design, Industrial--Social aspects--
Congresses. I. Bicknell, Julian. II. McQuiston,
Liz. III. London. Royal College of Art.
IV. International Council of Societies of
Industrial Design.
TS171.A1D464   745.2   77-3060
ISBN 0-08-021500-9

In order to make this volume available as economically and rapidly as possible the authors' typescripts have been reproduced in their original form. This method unfortunately has its typographical limitations but it is hoped that they in no way distract the reader.

*Printed and bound in Great Britain by
Butler & Tanner Ltd, London and Frome*

"We're not in this for the money - we're in it for life." Anon

We have two things to offer the emergent world: our
technology - a power for good as well as evil - and the frail
but real advantages of democracy. But if the rest of the world
is to learn from us, we must prove ourselves worthy of the
role of teacher. This is not a task for the weak - for those
who would opt out of society. It is simultaneously a political,
economic and social task which needs a toughness equal to
that of those who care only for the satisfying of their own
gluttony.

From the closing remarks to the Design for Need Symposium
by Sir Misha Black OBE RDI Hon DrRCA Hon D Tech
Joint Chairman of the Organising Committee.

CONTENTS

2   Contents

Photographs from the Atelier Bernard Lassus - pages 85 and 87.

Photographs by Tom Picton - pages 8,137,138,144 and endpiece.

Photographs by Mark Pilkington - pages 5,80,90,120,138 and 144.

FOREWORD
Prof. Frank Height, Joint Chairman of the Organising Committee

The idea for Design for Need - originally thought of as Design Action - came from many sources. There was the disquiet among professional and student designers about the lack of opportunities to use their talents in ways that were socially useful. There was the growing realisation among engineers that their professional code, based almost entirely upon technical innovation, efficiency and expansion, is incomplete without regard to the wider consequences of their work. There was the general awareness of the growth of waste and pollution, of the finite stock of mineral resources, of the neglect and destruction of the environment and of endemic problems such as those of the poor nations of the world and on a smaller scale, but much nearer home, those of elderly or handicapped people.

Design, whilst being an agency for so much benefit to the human race, nevertheless was seen, in its blind application of large scale technology, to be responsible for creating new problems as fast as it was solving others - and, in its neglect of the smaller miseries of life, was failing to intervene to help those who were disadvantaged in the tough regime of the modern world.

In the face of this evidence of design misapplication and neglect, industrial design in particular seemed to be most vulnerable to criticism. The philosophical roots of industrial design, unlike the more practical beginnings of engineering, are in the writings of men of social and aesthetic ideals, typically William Morris. The concept of design as a conditioning and reformist element in society, as well as a practical one, has persisted throughout the modern movement, emerging notably in the Bauhaus.

It seemed that the challenge to industrial design, in view of its aims, could not go unexamined - neither could the corresponding challenge to engineering and architecture.

It was resolved therefore to hold a symposium and exhibition at the Royal College of Art, where the question of the Social Contribution of Design would be examined, both at a general philosophical level and more importantly, by the demonstration and discussion of actual projects carried out in response to social needs.

To assist in this a theoretical study group of students from the School of Industrial Design was set up to monitor the proceedings. In particular they hoped to analyse: the fields in which projects of a Design for Need nature were at present being carried out; the kinds of design contribution being made (particularly the qualifications and experience of the designers and the nature of their work in innovating, adapting or refining technologies, in developing systems, or in simply providing more humane solutions); the kinds of organisation concerned and the various forms of financial support which have been obtained; new theoretical concepts, if any and proposals for future development.

The field was divided for analysis into four areas which seemed to form logical groupings for future study. These were:

> RESOURCES - studies in the effective use or reclamation and recycling of material resources, conservation of energy and the development of alternative sources.
>
> ENVIRONMENT - studies in the environmental consequences of design, and in conservation and regeneration.
>
> AID - studies in the provision of devices to aid individuals, for example the handicapped, sick or elderly, or other areas of neglect and (on a more general scale) disaster relief equipment.
>
> DEVELOPMENT - studies in industrial and agrarian developments in poor countries; the regeneration of depressed regions in industrialised countries; studies in education.

Following the symposium it has been decided to incorporate studies in these fields into the work of the School of Industrial Design at the Royal College of Art. This represents one of the useful results of Design for Need and is one which will provide a means for the extended and systematic study and development of design applications to projects of social value, and to underlying concepts of conservation and regeneration.

I would like to thank; the Royal Society of Arts, the Design Council, the Design and Industries Association, and the Society of Industrial Artists and Designers for both joining in the Organising Committee and for contributing funds; the International Council of Societies of Industrial Design and the International Council of Graphic Design Associations for taking part in the planning and publication of the event; UNESCO for the provision of a grant to enable speakers from developing countries to attend; and to the following firms and organisations who provided financial sponsorship - Courtaulds Ltd, National Fund for Research into Crippling Diseases, The Goldsmiths Company, King Edward's Hospital Fund for London, London Transport Executive, Commercial Union Assurance Ltd, The Financial Times, The John Lewis Partnership Ltd, Letraset International Ltd, The Wallpaper Manufacturers Ltd, British Olivetti Ltd, Unilever Ltd and Alfred Dunhill Ltd.

Lastly, I would like to thank my colleagues and students at the Royal College of Art who worked so hard to make Design for Need possible.

EDITORS' NOTE

This selection from the papers presented at the Design for Need Symposium at the Royal College of Art in April 1976 is by no means comprehensive. Of the fifty-two papers presented forty-six survived as typescript or tape and of those only twenty-four are presented here.

In preparing them for press we have tried to produce a representative anthology of the ideas that gave the event its special character. Many of these ideas are fundamentally important and it has been our aim to present them economically and forcefully so as to attract the widest attention. With this in mind we have not only omitted half the papers but we have cut and recast those we have chosen. In doing so we have attempted to avoid repetition and generally reduce the bulk of the available material for easy reading. Nevertheless we must take the blame for unforgiveable omissions or errors of fact.

We trust that those who prepared papers for the Symposium will approve the liberties we may have taken. For those with a more scholarly interest the original material will be preserved at the Royal College of Art for reference and republication.

Our thanks are due to the Design for Need Organising Committee and Sponsors as well as to Ann Dawkins who has patiently typed every word of this book several times.

Julian Bicknell and Liz McQuiston
Royal College of Art, October 1976

INTRODUCTION
Prof. Christopher Cornford, Symposium Organiser

The event of April 1976 at the Royal College of Art should be seen as part of a continuum. None too soon, but possibly just in time, members of the learned and skilled professions are waking up to an understanding of the disaster-course the world is set on by those who at present control it, insofar as anyone can be said to do so.

Scientists and technologists, increasingly since the Pugwash Conference of 1955 and the foundation in Britain in 1969 of the Society for Social Responsibility in Science, have been asking themselves: is it a good use of our knowledge and skills to devise nuclear bombs, defoliants, bacteriological weapons, counter-ecological pesticides, techniques for psychological coercion or genetic control and other such inhumanities?

The design and environmental planning professions, perhaps because their operations, when noxious, are less obviously so than those commissioned from science and technology by military-industrial complexes, have arrived somewhat more recently at the equivalent examination of conscience. Should they deploy their talents on the design, styling or promotion of products that are a superfluous pampering of the already over-provided; that waste non-renewable resources; that destroy amenities; that pollute cities and countryside; that exacerbate acquisitiveness and status-seeking; that alienate man from nature and man from man; that poison, enfeeble or distort our bodies and debase our minds - whilst simultaneously and by default allowing those devices (and advices) to go undesigned, unmade and undistributed that might help 'the wretched of the earth' (who far outnumber the even moderately provided) to grapple some way out of their misery?

More and more designers are answering no. As the invitation brochure to Design for Need put it:

> 'There is a worldwide concern that, despite the material benefits arising from advanced technology and industry, there is a deterioration in the quality of life and failure in the provision of many essential needs. This is accompanied by an increasing awareness of a waste of resources and a despoliation of the environment.'

And we went on to speak of:

> '... a return to the earlier ideals of the profession of industrial design which aimed to meet the needs of the modern world by designing in human terms where social purpose combined with aesthetic expression and symbolic value.'

7

All too obviously, given the way the world is heading, what will be needful if these
counsels are to prevail, is a vast, long-drawn-out campaign on many simultaneous
fronts, of which the Design for Need symposium and exhibition was an engagement
on the way. It gathered together men of goodwill amongst designers from all over the
world: the warmth of their presence, the fertility of their ideas, the urgency of their
vision and enthusiasm.

Obviously, too, the problem is not restricted to 'design' in the ordinary usage of
that word. It is not only new kinds of things that need to be invented: for if our systems
and institutions as found, fail to make the new things or actually prevent them being made
and/or distributed to those who need them, why then it is the systems and institutions
that call for redesign as much as their characteristic products. In other words, the
campaign must be fought in the educational and political spheres concurrently with
the technical, as indeed was stressed by many speakers at the symposium.

For one participant at least, the single most heartening feature of those three
memorable days was the presence (to say nothing of the quality of his contribution) of
an activist from a Trade Union whose members are among the most skilled workers
in the country: for it seems probable that only when those engaged in actual production
join hands with concerned designers in criticising our present practices and proposing
better ones, will there be an effectually massive force for change. I hope and believe
that this was the first bud in a new Spring.

What the editors present here can only be a sample of all that was said and put on
view at the event itself, but it is as representative of the spirit of the occasion as,
within the prevailing constraints, they have been able to make it. Their hope, and the
hope of everyone concerned, is that this set of excerpts will stimulate and encourage
like endeavours elsewhere and contribute to the momentum of an already considerable
reorientation of design activity.

OPENING ADDRESS
Sir Brian Flowers

I have to confess that I do not quite know what this Symposium is about. When Sir Misha
Black first asked whether I would speak at the opening session I looked through the
proposed list of topics and noticed that the greater number of them were being worked
on in some significant way at Imperial College. It is work being done by engineers,
or sometimes by scientists; and some of it is very close to what you seem to be
discussing here. For instance, we have a lot of interest in environmental technology,
in the design of artificial joints for arthritic patients, the development of new materials
and their use in engineering practise, the rehabilitation of mining land, the conservation
of energy resources; and we are deeply involved in technological education in India. So,
wishing to be good neighbours, we arranged a meeting betweeen some members of our
two Colleges to see whether there was a part that Imperial College engineers could
play. We found that on the whole there was not - or they would not - and so there are
few of us here today. And the reason was, they could not see what the Symposium was
about. In their eyes it seemed to be more of a 'happening' than a Symposium. We
were apparently intended to talk about the design aspects of an enormous range of more
or less haphazard subjects in the hope that something coherent might emerge. The
engineers, I suppose, felt that engineering is too disciplined a set of subjects to treat
in such a serendipitious fashion. Try as they might, our colleagues from the two
Colleges - who at the social level get on famously, admire and respect each other
professionally, and are even proposing to introduce joint courses in industrial design -
failed to make any dent on their mutual incomprehension.

Now, I tell you this tale more in sorrow than in anger - for I am not one who believes
in there being two cultures, or that poets are essentially different from physicists, or
artists from engineers - although I sometimes wonder about architects. One has only
to go round the Science Museum nearby, watching individual reactions to some marvel
of engineering: the word 'beautiful' is the one that occurs most often; and the more
cleverly, appropriately and economically the design satisfies its intended task the more
'beautiful' the object appears to be. I am not a moral philosopher any more than I am
an engineer, so I will not speculate on whether designers of machines are motivated by
intuitive feelings for abstract beauty, or whether it is merely a matter of semantics so
that something that is appropriate and economical, and therefore well-designed, is
automatically beautiful. But I do not consider that matters of taste kept us apart at our
meeting, nor even the objective. We all understood the objective well enough. There
is widespread disatisfaction with science and technology due to the fact that people
have come to feel that in some way it threatens them more than it helps them. High
technology has become a major matter of governmental and international policy. It
appears to respond only to the impersonal forces of economics and politics; it seems
blind to its effects on individual people; it thunders past, shaking our windows,
distrubing our sleep at night, and polluting the air we breathe.

9

Of course, that is a grossly unfair picture. When by simply pressing a switch we flood our sitting room with light, or bring ourselves through television into contact with the outside world, and when by sprinkling a fertiliser we reduce famine, and by swallowing a pill we fend off death, we are relying as individuals upon this same high technology that previously offended us. We choose to ignore the good in our annoyance with the bad. Disbenefits are all.

One really cannot have it both ways; but that is not to say that adjustments cannot be made, nor even that major changes of direction cannot be achieved. The older generations, in the industrialised countries at least, have been deeply affected by two World Wars and perhaps by a number of subsidiary ones. In our minds, at least, the priorities for science and technology are still largely those that result more or less directly from the stimulus of war: jet transport, nuclear power, sophisticated communications systems, and man-made substitutes for natural materials - all energy-intensive. There's nothing like war for spurring us on, and blinding us to what the peace might be like. Its aftermath lasts long. We must have Concorde to keep the aerospace industry in being, else we may not be able to defend ourselves. And as long as the threat of war hangs over us such arguments retain their validity. Should technologists then devote themselves rather more to pursuits that are deliberately chosen to reduce world tension? Is it possible that this is what our Symposium is about

And then, together with the major technological innovations I have mentioned, there has been the struggle for economic growth, for increased productivity with all its physical solutions dependent upon automation and the demand for higher skills from a labour force that only slowly adapts to the new requirements. Could there be something wrong with economic theories that require massive unemployment to solve our problem High technology seems at present to demand such a course. Might it not be better to choose a technological path based instead on full employment and human dignity? Could that be what this Symposium is about?

I also mentioned that most of these technological innovations are energy-intensive. One hears this phrase a lot nowadays, and we are all convinced that we have to save more energy. The trouble is that to do so significantly does not just mean switching off the lights when we leave the room, although that certainly helps a bit. It means a major reorientation of the whole approach to energy usage. For example, in the modern British home a quarter or more of the energy is used in the form of electricity; indeed, some people boast of their all-electric homes. But only a few per cent of the energy is really needed in this form - for lighting and useful electrical gadgets like refrigerators, razors and television sets. It need not be used at all for heating and cooking, except possibly in emergency. Electricity may be convenient for heating, but it is extremely inefficient in terms of the primary fuel used to produce it. Power stations burn about three kilowatts of fossil fuel in order to produce one kilowatt of electricity. To do away with this waste of two kilowatts, however, is not so simple. It is no good going back to burning coal in the grate because that also is an inefficient process. One needs district heating systems, and if one runs them from the reject hea of power stations one can get the most out of the fuel we burn so profligately. They do just this in many other European cities, so why not here too? And, of course, we can insulate our houses much better so that they stay warm with less energy consumption. But as we may hear during the Symposium, that means designing houses rather different

The world is burning up its resources fast. Our much-vaunted oil, much of it already mortgaged to those who are paying us to live above our means, will not last long into the 1990's. We can expect chronic difficulties thereafter, unless in the meantime we change our ways, for there are difficulties with the alternatives we speak about so eagerly. Is that what the Symposium is about?

Sir Alan Cottrell has recently summarised it all in a lecture to the Institution of Electrical Engineers. There are three daunting problems facing this Earth. Firstly, there is the problem of what our resources really are and whether there is any way of tapping more efficiently the energy of the sun. Secondly, the world's relentless population growth poses the dilemma of high-productivity farming which by its nature is highly vulnerable and so reduces our safety margins. Thirdly, for Western countries at least, wealth-creation techniques arrived before the population explosion, so that most technology has been directed towards labour-saving, energy-consuming, capital-intensive industries.

So now the trend must be reversed so that, for example in Britain where we shall otherwise continue to suffer from unemployment and the inability to pay for raw materials, there will have to be a shift to industries that depend more upon the skills of its people than on the mechanical consumption of energy and materials. Even more, in the power countries they will need low-capital industries, and we shall have to stop trying to export our high technology to them.

None of this can be achieved by simply ceasing to be technological. We cannot now 'stop the world and get off'. We shall need more technology, not less. But it will have to change its direction, towards something the world can better sustain. Is that what this Symposium is about?

I suppose that the Symposium is about all these things. Why then was there so little enthusiasm from my engineering colleagues at Imperial College for the Symposium as described to them by the Royal College of Art? I suppose it was because, by and large, Imperial College looks at these matters from the point of view of large-scale industry while the Royal College of Art, in organising the Symposium, has been seeing it more from the point of view of the individual - from the opposite end of the telescope, so to speak. We would have chosen the grander themes and followed them logically through to their application; in your Symposium you have chosen a set of disparate examples of human needs that call for new approaches and are trying to work back to find new principles.

Perhaps our engineers have become too accustomed to expecting people to adapt to what industry already has to offer to be ready to question the basic rightness of the whole system. Perhaps we identify ourselves too much with the high-pressure sales-manship with which industry preserves its status quo. After all, we nowadays teach our engineers the techniques of management and marketing as well as design. We move in a world in which it is still believed that what is good for General Motors is good for the United States.

And for his part, perhaps, the man in the street, whose life is increasingly stressful, too readily dismisses the enormous problems - political, economic, social - of bringing about a major change of direction in a highly technological society. And you at the Royal College of Art - you encourage him, you use your privilege of being artists to question the established rightness of things, you subvert the industrial society, you propose alternatives.

So it is a pity that more of my engineering colleagues are not here to contribute their bit of common sense and their enormous skills. There are, of course, a few: and I salute them for their good sense. But the ones who didn't come - they are the people you have to influence. You cannot do without them however right you are.

If there is to be a reorientation of the technological society - and I believe there has to be - it is going to involve all of us - engineers, artists, scientists, economists, educators, industry, Parliament and people. We shall have to create new relationships and new influences, new channels of communication, new knowledge and new skills, if we are to adapt the genius of all our peoples to meet the needs of the world in the Twenty-first Century.

PRECARIOUSNESS AND AMBIGUITY: INDUSTRIAL DESIGN IN DEPENDENT COUNTRIES
Gui Bonsiepe

Industrial design in dependent countries is a gloomy reality - a reality barely camouflaged by that well meaning optimism which, with an occasional condescending gesture, assigns to these peripheral economies the attribute 'developing'. Faced with the question 'What can industrial designers really do to satisfy the basic needs of those hundreds of millions of submerged people in the dependent world?' we probably have to answer 'Nothing' or 'Almost nothing'. That this applies to other professions too offers no consolation.

Critical designers today have lost the innocence that assumed one can influence social organisation through man-made objects or 'hardware artefacts'. Revolutions are definitely not achieved through objects and even less through 'designed' objects. Nevertheless, there are options in industrial design policy offering a choice of objectives toward which design activity can be directed. By formulating these object-ives and expressing aims in precise terms we can detect which design practice enhances and increases underdevelopment and dependence, and which design practice reduces them. For whatever the orientation of the design profession it is necessarily progressive or regressive, promoting or preventing social justice.

The web of political implications into which we in dependent countries stumble is more tangible than in central countries and derives from current global organisation, particularly the enormous inequalities in the distribution of wealth, caused by and - what is even worse - perpetuated through a system of unequal exchange or 'value transfer' from peripheral to central economies. As we shall see the role of the industrial designer on the periphery is deeply affected by these power relations and reference to the politics of industrial design in peripheral countries is not empty verbosity.

A plethora of books and articles has been produced analysing the historical reasons for underdevelopment and - to a lesser degree - why underdevelopment continues and increases in spite of officially anointed 'development decades'. It is clear by now that underdevelopment is not a prelude to development, nor a kind of toll a society has to pay to reach the expressway or snail path of development. On the contrary, underdevelopment is the sad corollary of development of central economies. The dependent subworld is the dark basement on which the central world rests.

In the sixties the capital inflow from central economies was roughly \$10,000 US per annum whereas the average return was at least fifty per cent more. The dependent countries finance their increasing underdevelopment. And in the same way that underdevelopment is the shadow image of development, industrial design on the periphery is the dialectical counterpart of industrial design at the centre.

13

Admittedly it would be unfair to deny that during the last ten years industrial design
has advanced considerably in dependent countries, whether for good or ill. Design
organisations have been established. Technical assistance programmes run by multi-
or bi-lateral organisations have been realised to spell out the gospel of good design.
Scholarships have been made available to industrial design students from peripheral
countries. Design promotion programmes have been sponsored by local governments,
above all in semi-industrialised countries and export oriented economies. New
technological policies which embrace industrial design have been propagated - under
slogans such as 'appropriate' and 'intermediate' technology. Though their starting
points differ, all these unorthodox technological policies meet at a concern for social
issues and environmental sensibility. But, although much goodwill has been accum-
ulated sometimes in good words and sometimes in better actions, we still lack a
critical evaluation of these projects - their successes and above all their failures.

But these achievements compare poorly with what still has to be done both in quantity
and quality. The realities of dependent countries present the discomforting and
depressing aspects of human life - or better, of attempts at human survival: lack of
shelter, lack of food, lack of productive work, lack of sanitation in growing urban
agglomerations, lack of adequate tools and machines. In the face of these discomforting aspects we must question both the content and orientation of industrial design as
we know it in central countries. We can hardly preserve that self-protective ignorance
towards the profession that a few years ago allowed an industrial designer to boast
that 'industrial design is a viable, intellectual, highly esteemable profession that
adds spice, interest, convenience and beauty to our industrial mode of living' (1).
In dependent countries the problem is not to add spice or interest or whatever to a
mode of living but to make survival possible, to provide a life support structure.
The central needs of the peripheral countries are the opposite of the peripheral needs
of the central countries.

Despite efforts to the contrary, industrial design in central economies is all too often
concerned with ephemeral product differentiation; that is 'a polite term for irrelevant
or marginal changes in a product for the purpose of creating new markets without
basic new production costs' (2). The industrial designer is not to be blamed that he
has few opportunities beyond product differentiation nor that it is often more profitable to design dazzling, spicy, sophisticated and tasteful products for an affluent
minority than to satisfy basic needs in sanitation, nutrition, health, transport, communication and production for the majority. This holds true for both central and
peripheral countries, for the First World too harbours its own 'Third World' or
marginal and under-privileged groups.

Central economies put a heavy emphasis on individual consumption and privately owned
artefacts. They accept and register needs preferably when these needs can be
satisfied by objects in the form of merchandise, ie products and services bought via
a social institution called market and possessed by individual consumers. Some
industrial designers consider it their prime task to promote sales. They seem quite
happy with that raison d'etre for their professional activity: 'In industrial design as
in sales, it's the curve that counts' (3).

This statement has the merits of all open confessions. It helps to explain in part why, in peripheral countries industrial design often plays a restricted role, catering for the needs of the higher income classes, limiting itself mainly to the perfection of the glamourised micro-environment of the homes of those who can pay for leather chairs, crystal lamps, stereo sets, linen curtains, stainless steel cutlery and executive desk sets. Of course there are masses, according to some too many masses. But there are in peripheral countries virtually no mass markets for designed products. The mass needs remain latent because income disbalance prevents their translation into effective demand. I see no way of reaching the needs of under-privileged people at subsistence level directly through industrial design efforts. This is not to be taken as a fatalist acceptance of the status quo; on the contrary. However it would be misleading to foster illusions of the potential social relevance of industrial design in peripheral countries so long as they suffer from abysmal internal inequalities.

In Latin America for example we can detect two mainstream influences: on one side the 'cultured' interpretation of industrial design of European coinage; that is the well-known concern for a marriage between culture and business, injecting the world of industrial production with a dose of taste to cure its supposed barbarisms; and on the other side the 'sales promotional' interpretation mainly (though not exclusively) associated with US business thinking. Both interpretations are in my view incompatible with the needs of dependent countries where self-based development is the aim. The problem is not to do with dissuading business men from making a profit, but with guaranteeing use-value to the consumer. The problem is not to do with persuading business men to opt for 'non-designed' products but with finding out which designed objects are socially relevant.

To evaluate the possibilities for industrial design we must look at the typical composition of industry in dependent countries. First I must mention the global corporations, although it is not my intention to mount a methodical attack on these institutions and their controversial role in dependent countries. They have branch plants which import their technology - including their industrial design - exclusively from the centre. So far these corporations have shown no major interest in transferring the skills of technological innovation, including the capaicty for local industrial design, to the periphery because technological innovation is one means to expanding and maintaining their power in dependent countries. They need to maintain and extend this power because they need the raw materials, the cheap labour and the 'pollution havens' of dependent countries. Of course they also want a foot in potential markets. As a rule technology is imported without questioning the compatibility of the technology with local needs, customs, climate, resources etc. Very little is to be expected of global corporations towards the promotion of local industrial design because they have a congenital hostility towards any local autonomous technological development.

Second, we find a series of big national industries owned either by local capital or government. And finally we have the numerous medium and small scale industries fading out to the artisan workshops. Only in exceptional cases does the local business man consider technological innovation his task. Technology rarely enters the focus of his attention except in terms of buying or copying.

The private investor too looks for short term returns on his investment. For that reason he favours investment in light industries, ie production of durable consumer goods for local middle and upper class. Since, in the Latin American example, income is distributed in such a way that twenty per cent of the population gets sixty-five per-cent of the total income, the market for mass-produced items is limited and production tends to be geared to that stratum with sufficient purchasing power. These groups are generally fascinated by western consumption patterns, which they try to imitate.

I want to illustrate this issue with some simple data from a design exhibition. Twenty per cent of the firms participating belonged to the furniture industry (including office furniture); eight per cent represented textiles and carpets; twelve per cent glass and stoneware: seventeen per cent electronic consumer goods. With one exception there was a total absence of producers of capital goods such as agricultural equipment and tools, manufacturing and building machinery. The narcissistic pre-occupation with the perfection of the liveing room predominated.

This is partly due to the pattern of industrialisation in Latin America, starting in the thirties and gaining momentum through World War II. It was directed towards inport substitution. Today it is recognised that this policy has not led to the expected results:

> It did not pay sufficient attention to 'induced' imports, like special modern materials and semi-finished goods to manufac-ture substitution products. Thus one external dependence has been substituted for another.

> It gave too much emphasis to the production of durable consumer goods.

> It did not take into account the need to create basic industries.

So, both cultural and technological dependence and the tendency to invest in projects with a fast return, foster the design products for the upper strata of society in dependent countries. Though this tendency will not be stopped without a profound change in the social order and a corresponding reformulation of priorities, one must look for complementary ways of providing industrial design with a broader social relevance. A base for action of this kind can be found in government institutions, preferably institutes for technological research and development. As mentioned before, branch plants of global corporations concentrate their R & D activities at the centre. The monopoly of technical innovation is an important part of their growth and domination. Management of local industries is as a rule reluctant to finance technical innovation. For these reasons government support is indispensable to the creation of an institutional base for industrial design in dependent countries. In many cases the government already has a high share (sometimes more than fifty per cent) of the total investments (where in Europe this share is considerably lower - twenty to thirty per-cent). Furthermore, the relatively strong position of governments permists a concentration of R & D activity and the formulation of technological policy into which industrial design is integrated. Only local governments have sufficient force to counteract the foreign influences detrimental to the national economy. It is not by chance that global managers consider the nation state an obsolete institution hindering the free flow of capital, resources and technology. Nationalism, by definition a political ambition, is the only way for dependent countries to defend their interests and to substitute autonomy and interdependence for a state of being repeatedly sacked.

Nationalism should not be understood as a narrow-minded chauvinistic enterprise but as a crystalising point for identity; not as an expression of collective aggression, real or symbolic, but as a basis for non-violent communication.

One noted characteristic of dependent economies is their extreme vlunerability in the external sector. Economic activity has been geared to export prices determined to a great extent in the world's centres of decision. Economic planners should therefore insist on a pattern of industrialisation that promotes a self-centred or autonomous economy as against an outer-directed or dependent economy.

With the backing of this kind of policy, industrial design can contribute to the satisfaction of local needs preferably with local materials and locally developed technology. To be effective industrial design must be part of a general technological policy, ie a set of priorities for technical and industrial development with corresponding allocation of resources. These priorities may refer to food production, the use of alternative forms of energy, small scale manufacturing industry or social equipment. According to these priorities the designer would be involved in the development of agricultural tools and equipment, solar energy devices, metal and wood transforming tools and machines or school furniture. He would not only design but would also help to distribute knowledge to people so that they can produce the things they need themselves.

After project work there is a second important role industrial designers can assume in dependent countries. They can be involved in a special kind of technological evaluation concerning patents. Peripheral countries that subscribe to the international rules of industrial property protection, suffer all the disadvantages and none of the advantages of current patent law. Roughly ninety per cent of patents registered in dependent countries originate in central economies. Global corporations have used less than ten per cent of their patents on the periphery. Patents are mainly used for technological suppression rather than stimulating technological development. In order to counteract this harmful tendency governments on the periphery should impose strict regulations on foreign patents registration, requiring for instance the immediate application of the know-how contained in the patent. Protection should not be given to industrial models or designs and definitely not to 'brands'. Paying royalties for the design of a chair in hard or semisoft foreign exchange is effectively burning money. Famous though they may be, brands are not technology. They are fictitious technology - a fact that does not hinder foreign corporations from trying to sell brands as technology.

The selling of technology in the form of patents is - in cybernetic terms, a kind of variety reduction - leading to virtual monopoly. The industrial designer in contrast is or ought to be capable of producing variety or creating alternative.   If he is worth his name he will never be convinced that the optimal solution suggested by the patent is the only one. He is specially equipped to break the monopolistic tendencies of foreging technological imports. He can fill a role of strategic importance in technological evaluation by judging which patents are worth paying for and which should be rejected.

There also appears to be a strong case for labour intensive production in dependent countries, where unemployment sometimes reaches an astronomical figure between twenty and forty per cent. Labour costs are usually much lower than in central

countries: in Mexico for example the average hourly rate in the garment industry is
less than twenty-five per cent of that in the USA. Strong unions are almost unknown,
so local governments can advertise idyllic 'strike-free' paradises: Singapore for
instance guarantees five years without labour troubles to foreign investors. Even
without the 'export platforms' of foreign businesses a plea for labour intensive technologies may be well founded. However, such a policy rests on the assumption that
factor-intensity in the production of certain goods, let us say leather products,
remains the same in all countries competing for international markets. I quote:

> 'There is no guarantte for developing countries that a given
> product cannot be manufactured more cheaply for world
> markets by highly capital intensive methods in industrialised
> countries.' (4)

Factor-composition is flexible and can change rapidly through technological innovation
Advocates of labour-intensive production should take a certain care.

I want finally to tackle the relationship of industrial design at the centre to that at the
periphery, especially technological aid and 'aidism'. Industrial design has spread to
dependent countries through many different channels to produce a technological
transfer. According to my view however, there is only one form of effective design
transfer that is in the interests of dependent countries: design transfer that helps to
uncover and stimulate local design capacity, witohut paternalism. I am not yet sure
whether we will have to invent a new kind of practice of inverse industrial design to
undesign the environment and de-sophisticate artefacts.

Of course concern in the centre for the reality of the peripheral subworld is welcome,
but I doubt that we get to the core of the problem by starting to design 'for' dependent
countries. My summary based on eight years of continuous work in peripheral
countries is: 'Design for dependent countries', should read 'Design in dependent
countries' or 'Design by dependent countries'. The centre does not possess the
universal magic formulae of industrial design which have to be propagated to the
inhabitants of the periphery whom the intelligence agencies' ideology conceives as
underdeveloped 'wogs'.

Stafford Beer once wrote 'Homo faber sees the world in terms of the things he makes.
Making things is no problem any more. Homo faber is plain out of date' (5). Taken
at face value this is a laconic obituary to the industrial designer who after all is
essentially an 'object maker', whose activities are manifest in the material artefacts
of our environment. However this provoking assertion is more than a simple death
warrant. I think Professor Beer wanted to hint at the need to approach the environmen
not as an accumulation of separate objects but as a whole system, the parts of which
are related to the whole by certain rules. We may modify his statement: the second
generation homo faber does not see the world in terms of things but in terms of
needs to be satisfied. This is the prosaic challenge for future industrial design.

REFERENCES

(1) M G Grossman (Industrial Design, September 1970) p 10

(2) R J Barnet & R E Müller, Global Reach (Simon & Schuster, New York 1974) p 352

(3) E Bordinat Jr, It's the Curve that Counts in Industrial Design and its Relationship to the Arts (American Society of Industrial Designers, New York 1962)

(4) K Busch, Die Multinationalen Konzerne (Suhrkamp, Frankfurt/M 1974) p 88

(5) S Beer, Platform for Change (John Wiley & Sons, London, New York, Sydney, Toronto 1975) pp 25, 26

S Amin, El capitalismo periferico (Editorial, Nuestro Tiempo, Mexico 1974)

F Godard, Vom Bedürfnisbegriff zur Klassenpraxis (Marxismus Digest, September 1973) pp 3-29

I Illich, Selbstbegrenzung - Eine politische Kritik der Technik (Rowohlt, Reinbek 1975)

G Jones, Ciencia y tecnologia en los paises en desarrollo (Fondo de Cultura Economic, Mexico 1973)

V Navarro, Industrialismus als Ideologie (Technologie und Politik, July 1975)

T Szentes, Politische Okonomie der Entwicklungsländer (Europäische Verlagsanstalt, Frankfurt/M 1974)

J Strasser, Grenzen des Wachstumus - Grenzen der Freiheit? (Technologie und Politik, December 1975)

SOME ASPECTS OF AGRARIAN AND INDUSTRIAL DEVELOPMENT IN A DEVELOPING COUNTRY
Godfrey Semiti

My task will be to examine the problems facing agriculture and industry in a backward, non-industrialised economy, with particular reference to policies and planning. I shall attempt to show from general and specific examples why agriculture and industry have remained undeveloped in developing countries. I will discuss agriculture and industry together because these two sectors of the economy tend to remain divorced from each other in the national development plans of developing countries, with deplorable consequences. It is my belief that for a healthy socio-economic development the two sectors of industry have to enjoy sectoral equality.

The reason for this is that to modernise agriculture a given country requires certain inputs (such as tools) made by local industries. There will also be need for more roads, railways, dams and canals to support an expanding agriculture. And once agriculture has been improved and the productivity per acre and worker increased, there will be rural redundancy, and consequently the need for industry to absorb the surplus labour. (This in fact was the case in Great Britain during the Agrarian Revolution resulting from the Enclosure.)

As most of us will no doubt be aware, the backwardness of the economies of the Third World is not entirely accidental. During the time of their dependence, these countries of the Third World were meant to be sources of cheap raw materials for the industrialised countries. In other words, the producers of the raw materials did not benefit from their efforts. They were denied the value added to raw material resulting from manufacture. Unfortunately, however, this trend has continued after independence, as successive national development plans eloquently encourage agriculture and discourage industry.

The need to generate employment through industrialisation is emphasised by the fact that in developing countries the domestic market remains small and insignificant in spite of growing populations. In Tanzania for instance a World Bank Study of the economy in 1961 led to a surprising conclusion that the 'level of external and not domestic demand constituted the greater constraint on the expansion of agricultural output' - surprising because with a population of ten million people in Tanzania at that time, the potential domestic market was bigger than that of Sweden today. But the World Bank's study was based on valid data. If we take wage employment as a criterion of internal market for food supplies for instance, we find that this has been declining from 252,000 wage earners (5.4% of the population) in 1936 to 347,000 wage earners (2.9% of the population) in 1967. This is a serious trend indeed and may well be at the root of economic stagnation of the country.

The state of agriculture and industry in a developing country may be illustrated by Tanzania. In the first Ten Year Development Plan (1946-1956), the economy of

Tanganyika, as it was known then, is summarised: 'Tanganyika is a predominantly agricultural country, with considerable mining potentials still untapped. The basis of agriculture - land - must therefore be conserved, reclaimed and improved ... ' (1). The plan then elaborated the agricultural development to be undertaken. Efforts were to be made in the production of export cash crops such as sisal, cotton, coffee and oil seeds. Food crops however were to be largely left to take care of themselves.

The erratic and uncertain marketed production of food crops may well explain the unwillingness of subsistence farmers to become fully commercialised and depend on food purchases. Maize, for instance gives a sizeable per caput distribution of ten kilogrammes only once in fourteen years, and less than one kilogramme for ten years during the same period.

After independence in 1961, Tanzania had a look at her economic development, and for the first time the fatal neglect of industry was recognised. This is seen in the first Five Year Development Plan (1964-1969) in which the Minister of Economic Planning described the economy as unsatisfactory (2).

> 'If national income is taken to be determined by the levels of
> activity in primary production, manufacturing and marketing
> sectors, it will be seen that the past colonial period was
> essentially characterised by a development of the first of these
> factors, and by a relative stagnation of the other two.
>
> This one-sided development finds further expression in the fact
> that 80% non-food consumer goods purchased by Tanganyikans
> were imported, and that 90% of the foodstuffs consumed did
> not pass through any market channels whatsoever, remaining
> within the non-monetary, subsistence sector. The structural
> disequilibrium - reflected in the production mainly of agricultural
> raw materials for export, the importation of manufactured
> goods, and in the nation feeding itself mainly through subsistence -
> though common for most developing countries, is accentuated
> in Tanganyika. The economy of the country resembles a body,
> parts of which have developed normally, while other parts have
> suffered from atrophy due to lack of exercise ... '

The main point made here is the state of atrophy suffered by the industrial and marketing sectors of the economy. It is a pity, however, that despite this recognition the necessary de-atrophisation was not subsequently carried out.

Case studies carried out by Ruthenberg (3) in 1965-1967 give an excellent picture of the state of agriculture and industry in Tanzania. Altogether ten cases were studied, representing a whole range of ecological and demographic factors. It should be noted that Tanzania's agriculture is characterised by extremely low productivity, rampant unemployment and underemployment, and almost total absence of industries. The low productivity of Tanzania's agriculture is probably best highlighted by the fact that in 1972 the country had an estimated forty-nine million acres under cultivation, and yet she had difficulty in feeding her thirteen million people (4). In Ruthenberg's studies

rural labour utilisation is estimated to be 25%-57% of available labour, which shows
a very high incidence of unemployment and underemployment. Unfortunately however,
Ruthenberg's excellent analysis of small holder agricultural backwardness fails in one
important aspect. It does not attempt to bring in rural industries, if only to absorb
the idling labour. In my view, in cotton growing areas for instance, cottage textile
industries would not only absorb the idling labour but they would also produce linkage
industries. The rural industrial workers would also create a demand for food and thus
expand the domestic market. They could become village proletariats. They would in
the words of Lenin, 'form an alliance with the peasants'.

Planning and planning policies in developing countries as studied by Vente (5) are
irrelevant because they are drawn up by foreigners who are not familiar with the local
setting and who come from capitalist countries where central national plans are unknown
Consequently many plans in developing countries are not directed to the needs of the
indigenous people. On the contrary, they tend to assume an internalistic nature and
to serve the interests of industrialised, developed countries.

> 'Some newly independent governments are willing to go quite
> cynically through the motions of preparing and publishing a
> plan document, knowing that Development Plans are now
> regarded as evidence of respectability, as a basis for obtaining
> foreign aid ... in East Africa this belief is reflected by the
> fact that the first plans after independence were more or less
> rewordings of recommendations of the various World Bank
> Missions which had visited these countries ... '

Vente's observation is supported by Tanzania's Three Year Development Plan (1961-19
whose objectives on agriculture are stated as follows:

> 'The World Bank Mission assessed the main development of
> peasant agriculture ... It was their view and clearly the right
> one, that even if mineral production were to increase greatly
> in the coming years, the bulk of the population would continue
> to engage in agriculture ... '

There is a conspicuous silence on agricultural industries, food and nutrition, and
general industrialisation of the economy. Other significant omissions in the plan
are in connection with general education of the population. One finds a preference
for limited secondary education - unfortunate, considering the U N Declaration of
Human Rights on universal education.

The second Development Plan (1964-1969) did make a declaration to deatrophise the
economy and initiate industrialisation. Unfortunately however, the industrial policy
adopted is not based on the resources and needs of the country. On the contrary, the
industrial policy is based on import substitution of consumer goods enjoyed by a tiny
elite. It is not surprising therefore that in the plan under question (1964-1969), the
domestic market for agricultural products is considered to be insignificant, and the
export market is advocated as the major constraint on the expansion of agriculture.

The plan gives projected annual production and consumption of consumer goods in Tanzania for 1980. If we take food for instance, it provides for a per caput annual production of sixteen kilogrammes of meat and 5.3 gallons of milk; and on the industrial plane 1/3 of a pair of shoes; 1.7 pints of beer; 2.3 sq yds of fabric and 2.1 kilogrammes of steel. At this rate one cannot think of clothing every Tanzanian adequately, or providing him with a pair of shoes in the present century; nor can one think of providing an iron-roofed house for each family for several centuries. The plan therefore bears no relationship to the declared political policy of working for social justice and equality in so far as major necessities of life are concerned. In short, the plan ignores the needs of the people, and consequently all we can expect is stagnation.

I am now going to suggest a possible therapeutic treatment. You will note I am saying a possible treatment because the backwardness of agriculture and industry in developing countries is still largely an incurable cancer. But with a bit of luck, and depending on the response of the patient, we may strike the one chance in ten thousand of real recovery.

Our first task is to 'de-internationalise' the economy of the country and direct our priorities to the needs of the people and their full satisfaction. In other words, we have to direct the economy towards the maximum exploitation of the domestic market, and thereby achieve full utilisation on the entire labour force. We have to help the people to help themselves - the principle of community development.

Professor Sir Joseph Hutchinson has identified a basic fact about rural communities:

> 'Rural communities do not work to benefit the society or nation
> (or worse, international communities); they work to improve
> their own lot and in so doing they contribute to nation building' (6).

Secondly, we have to de-atrophise those sectors of the economy which have suffered decay through disuse. We have to develop industries, building and construction, transport and communications and the internal market, in a proper balance with agriculture. The myth we so often hear, that developing countries cannot industrialise because they have small domestic markets and therefore cannot benefit from economies of scale, has to be discarded. After all, the industrial revolution was born in Britain when her population was five million people and in the US four million. The population of Tanzania at fifteen million is the same as that of Britain in about 1845 when the latter was industrialised to over-flowing. (Of course, the industrialisation of the US was in part the cause of a political revolution and the war of independence two hundred years ago today. Fortunately, it is no longer necessary to have such a revolution to industrialise, thanks to increased international co-operation.) All that is required is a political will, the willingness to import technology (at a price) and the ability to formulate a rational plan.

Which brings me to the third and final prerequisite for an integrated agrarian and industrial development. We need proper plans, which require technology and experience. In drawing up such plans we should ideally use experts who have the local knowledge and they should work out plans in adequate time, not as visiting missions on flying visits.   As W Luttrel pointed out; our industrial and agricultural plans can start with low forecasts, build up markets, and then grow to reasonable size.   This was in fact the case with Britain which started with steel production of five hundred tons in 1717 and grew to 240,000 tons ninety years later.   More recently, in 1949 China started blast furnaces in communes and now she is exporting steel.   While nearer home, we have old people in Tanzania who remember working in village iron foundries at the beginning of this century who were unfortunately forced out of their industry.

In this paper I have attempted to analyse the present state of agriculture and industry in Tanzania, a newly emergent developing country which has continued to orient her economy externally to overseas markets rather than internally to the needs of her people.   In doing this I hope to stimulate the action required to change agriculture and industry so as to balance the socio-economic development of the peoples of the Third World - an equilibrium indispensable to world peace and security.

REFERENCES

(1) Ten Year Development Plan for Tanganyika 1946-1956
    (Government Printer, Dar es Salaam)

(2) First Five Year Development Plan for Tanganyika 1964-1969
    (Government Printer, Dar es Salaam)

(3) H Ruthenberg, Small-holder Agriculture and Small-holder
    Development in Tanzania (Weltforum Verlag, Munchen)

(4) Siasa ni Kilimo - Agricultural Policy Paper (Tanganyika
    African National Union 1972)

(5) R Vente, Planning and Planning Processes - The East African
    Case (Weltforum Verlag, Munchen)

(6) I H Cox, The World Land Use Survey: Occasional Paper No 7
    (Geographic Publications Ltd, 1968)

INDENTIFICATION OF DESIGN PROBLEMS IN INDIA
Professor Sudhakar Nadkarni

Twenty-nine years have passed since India became independent. Before independence the mood of the younger generation was entirely concentrated on achieving full political freedom. After achieving independence we had a new generation of Indians on the scene. Their aspirations enshrined in the constitution became the keynote of the conception of their birthright and their birthright was total welfare. Today, they are keen to see an all-round national development

India has a population exceeding six hundred million, spread over an area of 326,800,000 sq kilometres. Of this only 18% is urban, while the rural population is distributed in more than 567,000 villages. The general literacy rate is around only 25%. The income of at least 33% of the rural population and 50% of the urban population is below poverty level.

Since independence India has made impressive progress in the industrial sector and its net output has risen more than fourfold over the period 1947-74. The progress made has been even greater when judged in terms of the range and sophistication of the products manufactured.

But in spite of this magnificent technological achievement, endeavours to reach the poor have not been successful. An eminent scientist, K N Reddy, points out:

> 'Western technology has buttressed the polarisation of Indian
> society with a small, comparatively rich, acquisitive,
> conspicuously consuming, politically powerful, city-centered
> elite, drawing its ideas and values from the West, and a
> large mass of poor people left out of the circle of production
> and consumption by lack of employment and purchasing power.'

If real democracy means the well-being of the majority, we cannot afford to forget Gandhi's accent on developing the village economy and the importance of spending a considerable part of our resources on medium and low-technology items which will provide the poor rural masses with the minimum needs of survival.

Our discipline demands a certain conception of human values in which technological and economical values are supreme along with cultural values. Therefore, I have aimed at rural India to pave the way for economical and technological changes of a certain type. I would refrain from enforcing the stamp of an urban elite or industry-based cultural norm, with their inherent concepts of functionality and aesthetic value, on the problems of rural design. When people are hungry, the immediate pressure to find an earning opportunity is far greater than the effect of promises, even in the near future, of earning and stability.

The introduction of new technology in rural areas is itself no solution to the problem of rural poverty and unemployment. What is needed is an integrated programme of rural development. Non-agricultural development and the growth of social and cultural services are as important as agricultural development. The emphasis should be on a programme of co-ordinated agricultural/industrial development. This could include diversification of agriculture, rural public works, setting up agro-processing industries and local manufacturing units for the supply of inputs, decentralisation of light industries to rural areas and provision of trading, banking and social service facilities.

Furthermore, the prime necessity in rural areas is the creation of jobs in order to integrate the population in productive activities. One of the main possibilities is through design input, of whatever type. New activities can be generated through design input, adding value to the local resources. The added values can be retained in the area to increase the income of the population. Such activities should have a relatively simple technological base so that the educational system can generate the skills required increasing the number of trained people and, thereby, the local production base. The education-cum-training base should be made as self-reliant as possible by training local people who will subsequently train others. The whole economic-cum-education effort should be self-governing and self-regulatory, perhaps through co-operative organisation.

With the introduction of new designs, including art and craft activities, a number of allied trades can provide better employment opportunities. Take for example, trades like textile dyeing or weaving. Weaving, dyeing or stitching can be taught to others. A textile designer who can advise on new designs, prints or patterns is usually conversant with manufacturing and processing techniques and can pass on his know-how to create new trades. The same will be the case with any other design input such as pottery, toy or tool making.

The end result of the design input should be the development of products. Whether they are agricultural or not, the products should be such that the community itself can make use, and earn from them. Here, the designer's scope is not limited to designing products. He may also design the simple tools to manufacture the products. To avoid exploitation by the middle man or the employer, the design development activity should be a self-generating process through co-operative means. The designer himself has to take the responsibility of training the illiterate and semi-literate rural masses.

It is very important that the designer becomes a part of that rural society, to win their confidence. He cannot do this alone. He has to take the assistance of other experts, such as economists, sociologists and administrators. It is absolutely neces- sary to create confidence amongst the local people and the politicians to speed up implementation. The designer has to recognise that the sense of traditional values is very strong among the rural millions. He must also recognise that folk art and craft are created by indigenous designers and artists who are no less creative than the modern urban designer. When the conventional designer tries to bring to them the benefits of his better-informed and more analytic mind, he will have to concede to them their aesthetic imagination and skill. Thus, the designer working in the village area will have to keep in mind traditional and rural India with a view to synthesising traditic and modernity.

The creation of new employment potential with the introduction of design input will bring some technical and human constraints. Performance will depend greatly on the choice of technology. Preferences for technology and human resources while working for a rural community are:

> Approach to design innovation - capital saving and employment generating, rather than capital intensive and labour saving technologies.

> Products should be manufactured in the cottage scale and small scale rather than large scale technology.

> Consideration of simple technology and skills already available with the traditional rural craftsmen like potters, weavers, blacksmiths, carpenters, cobblers and tanners.

> Preference should be given to local materials rather than materials transported from a distance or urban areas.

> Production technology should be energy saving, rather than energy intensive - preference for locally made manure gas.

As the literacy rate is very low in rural areas, it is necessary to introduce design training at secondary school level for literate, semi-literate and illiterate people. In contrast to urban areas the material available is mostly natural and thus the choice is limited. The technological base is low and manpower is semi-skilled. Formal aspects of design play a secondary role. Unlike urban areas where the people are not prepared to settle for less if they can get the best, utility consumer goods are acceptable in rural areas.

The design process in urban areas starts from the briefing from the clients (the industries). In most cases data is available. A rural area, however, is entirely different in that the designer himself has to select the problem, collect the data and find the solution through inter-disciplinary efforts. With this in mind, I suggest the following prerequisites:

> The designer's main objective should be creation of jobs by generating new design activity.

> He should have first-hand knowledge of organisational structure (government, local government) and political groups in the area he chooses to work (and their sympathetic co-operation).

> Collection of basic data on available natural resources, need-oriented analysis and evaluation, and finally, determination of end-use.

> Work through institutions, government agencies, voluntary organisations or individuals. Gaining confidence of officials and political channels is essential.

> As his living will depend on his design service for urban industries, he should be able to pay frequent visits to the rural

areas of his choice (his semi-voluntary service).

He should be able to convince the villagers that his projects
need their full participation and co-operation, as the villagers
themselves will have to organise the scheme and pay for it.

He should also consult other experts connected with production,
such as marketing personnel, economists, and bankers, and
get their participation.

Once through the prerequisites, it is time for actual execution of the scheme. On
starting the scheme, there are two possibilities of scale, each having specific
qualities: Small scale; Cottage scale.

A small scale industry is one employing less than fifty persons, if operating with
power, and with capital assets not exceeding Rs. 5 lakhs at the initial stage. On the
other hand, a cottage industry is run wholly or partly with the help of the members of
a family in whole or part time occupation.

It is advisable to start the project on a cottage industry scale with five to ten villagers
forming a co-operative society. Forming a society generates unselfish spirit, and
the activity is conducted under democratic management. An isolated and poor individual
relying on the mutual support of others can procure the tools and equipment, which are
easily available to resourceful persons, and thereby develop himself to the fullest
extent of his capabilities. Design inputs can be introduced in several areas:

Textiles   - design of simple looms.

Textile Design - dyeing and processing techniques.

Woodworking - products for everyday use, toys, furniture,
                      agricultural tools.

Pottery

Metal Work   - design of domestic products.

Agricultural   - tools and transport.

In conclusion, I would like to reiterate what Gandhi said, 'India lives in her villages,
and if you want to improve her lot, you have to work with the people there and not
merely for the people there.' What I wish to project is that the designer should work
as a member of the village community, and not serve as a feeder to the community.
He has, of course, to enlist the co-operation of the various other agencies involved in
the implementation of his project, taking into account the specific requirements of the
rural community so that the output becomes the real in-product of the community.

DESIGN COLLABORATION AT THE INDIAN INSTITUTE OF TECHNOLOGY, NEW DELHI 1970-1972
Roger Breakwell and Roger Newport

In 1969, the Imperial College Delhi Committee started a programme in association with the Royal College of Art, whereby industrial designers were assigned to the Instrument Design Development Centre (IDDC) within the Indian Institute of Technology in New Delhi (IIT(D)). The collaboration was administered by what was then the Ministry of Overseas Development under the Colombo Plan. Roger Newport describes the programme and its background in 1970, and Roger Breakwell the programme in 1971.

The five Indian Institutes, at Delhi, Kanpur, Bombay, Madras and Kharagpur, were built and equipped with aid from a variety of countries, to provide 'Centres of excellence' for the teaching of technology. It is indicative of the Institutes' status that as many as 40,000 candidates have sat the competitive entrance examination for which there are 1,600 places. Compared with other disciplines in higher education, a large number of students in India are attracted to engineering. Strong imported European traditions have even resulted in the Anglo-Indian surname 'Engineer', similar to our 'Miller' or 'Thatcher'. Parents are convinced that their children would be better off in this field, despite the fact that there were an estimated 40,000 engineering degree and diploma holders out of work in 1969.

Britain's role in providing aid is an historic one and still very much in evidence, for instance the similarity in passenger car design. We discovered that attitudes to aid varied from enthusiastic, political or sometimes philosophical acceptance, to outright rejection. An eloquent minority of academics were of the opinion that India should make her own mistakes even if they were the same ones that the more industrially developed nations had already learned the hard way; at least the initiative would be India's. Whatever the attitude to his work, the foreign advisor works within an administrative structure and, more generally a cultural system which is very different to the one in which he trained and practised. In our particular case, it was little consolation to learn that nearly everybody else in the new environment of the Institute felt a similar unease because of the enormous diversity of backgrounds which were represented.

Even an industry such as the agricultural machinery industry, forced as it was by the spotlight of government attention, was unable to fulfil the government's development plan, basically because its administrative structure was unable to meet the demands put upon it. A preliminary though comprehensive survey by the United States Agency for International Development (USAID) concluded that contributory causes were lack of basic knowledge, motivation, materials, communication and financing.

This introduction would seem to paint a rather jaundiced picture of a country which contains immense resources of manpower and cultural tradition; and these comments might seem a long way from the work of an industrial designer, but they set a scene

which concerned us more in the progress of our work as advisors than what we did
at the drawing board and in the workshop; primarily because any design work such as
that which we undertook, requires a lot of information, consultation and planning -
co-operation of every kind. Aspects of what we learned to ascribe to 'culture shock'
affected our work more than we realised at the time. Climate of course affected us
as well, and anyone who has tried to work at a drawing board during the monsoon
without air conditioning will know the conditions that make even a legible drawing so
difficult to produce. The normally available intermediate technology solution of
blowing air through wet khus grass only makes matters worse.

The first team of designers, David Weightman, Michael Parr and Roger Newport
with the invaluable presence of Bernard Myers, established that the brief was three-
fold: a) to act as design consultants to academic staff and students of the Institute,
b) to undertake lecture and tutorial work, and c) to redesign prototype scientific and
educational instruments so that they could be produced by the Centre's workshop or
by industry, for sale. The Institute had already published a catalogue of their prototype
scientific instruments, describing seventy-four major pieces of equipment.

One of the first projects we undertook (led by Michael Parr) involved the design of an
overhead projector, an item which up until then had been imported. It was designed
specifically for indigenous production mainly in order to save foreign currency.

Another early project, undertaken by David Weightman, was the development of an
indigenous language laboratory for use at village level. A government minister
had suggested the project, presumably with India's 826 languages and 1,652 Mother
Tongues in mind. India's national language - Hindi - is spoken only by twenty-six
per cent of the population. The first sketch proposals were based on Chinese experience with a purely acoustic system of things like doctors' stethoscopes, but this
proposal wasn't approved for further development. The basic idea was that units would
be cheap enough to set up in as many permanent local centres as possible. The second
series of proposals was obviously more expensive, based on indigenous cassette
recorders made under license, and suggested mobile facilities providing the same
for as little additional expense as possible. These proposals weren't taken any further
either and the reasons were never clear. However, we believe the Centre is still
interested in the project, and development hinges on unavailable cassette decks. It is
to be hoped that the present programme of satellite television direct to village
receivers, and increasing radio ownership will eventually ease the language problem.
It is probably already well known that the family planning programme with its slogan
"Two, No More', used to reward vasectomy patients with a transistor radio.

We also undertook a lecturing commitment at a summer school for engineeing
faculty from all over India, putting engineering in a context of entrepreneurship in an
attempt to reduce the number of unemployed engineers leaving colleges and the
Institutes. This proved to be a very successful exercise, bearing in mind the national
trait of theorising about a problem as the only respectable way of solving it. Indian
expertise with theoretical analysis is of course, very well known in many advanced
fields, and there are powerful cultural reasons for this. One of the more noticeable
is the attitude that to do anything with your hands is a socially demeaning activity, and
what social mobility there is tends to reinforce this propensity. However, the

summer school project groups did consider specific products, workshop layouts, break-even charts and one group even produced rough alternative sketch designs for a vacuum cleaner as a preliminary to costing. The other five project groups concerned themselves with the production of weighing scales and a pressure cooker, both of which were conventional designs, a power tiller, ready-made garments and plastic goods.

As a result of that school and a two year post-graduate course and the more general influence of the aid programme, design is at least a subject on the current under-graduate engineering syllabus.

We were designing for different levels and types of skill to those which are available in Britain, so traditional crafts were of great interest to us. The traditional pit firing of pots, or traditional jewellery manufacture was as much an indication of what was technically feasible as the modern concrete buildings or the motor vehicles.

The range of design options is enormous whatever type of artefact you consider, but then, the range of peoples and the range of traditions is enormous too. But until the people who are making those options choose from that superb range, instead of letting design decision rest on traditions of kinship or even the tradition of imported technology, there can never be practical realisation of the relationship between technology and society, and therefore never any possibility of choosing the future, let alone designing it.

This relationship points to another project: the redesign of a very simple micro-spinner producing prototype man-made fibres by means of a heated cylinder, a gravity fed piston and a series of interchangeable nozzles.

Man-made fibres form a complex alternative to the traditional cotton manufacturing industry which produced seventy-five million metres in 1969. Man-made fibres are still mostly vegetable rather than mineral based in India, so there is very little ground for the popular resource depletion argument. An enormous effort goes into the maintenance of cotton clothing, and the Dhobi or laundryman as well as the house-wife expends a lot of effort washing by the traditional battering method, leaving it to dry and bleach in the sun and then maybe ironing with a heavy charcoal-heated iron.

In a country with massive unemployment, do you develop a product which will put even more people out of work? Or do you consider it not only desirable and possible but also practical that they do something more useful? Do you introduce cheap ready made, easy wash, non-iron clothes and throw most of the nation's tailors and launderers out of work?

These are questions that cannot be answered until alternative products - alternative systems of fulfilling the same basic needs - are available for assessment. There can be no social determination of technology, at even the most basic level until alterna-tives are generated and there is a choice to make.

In February 1971, Roger Breakwell, Clive Garrard and Mike Warren took over work in the Design Centre. There was a residue of work awaiting production and it became important to produce more prototypes and items from the catalogue that were in demand.

In India the caste system draws clear distinctions between the thinker and the maker, probably it even creates these distinctions. There was little communication in the centre between indigenous designers and their technicians.

Much was spent in the workshop sorting out design and manufacturing problems. Some of the most valuable work was achieved with the technical staff - making, assembling and modifying designs as necessary, gradually eroding the conceit that the designer is above working with his own hands.

For instance a piece of equipment was developed for low temperature refining of organic semi-conductors. The material to be refined was placed in a tube, carried on a mechanically driven rack up and down a column. The tubes passed through a heating zone, cooled on either side by air. The rate at which the tube rack travelled had to be variable, together with the number of passes over the heaters. Soon after the prototype was in the workshop the original was found shrouded in black paper. It was being used to refine photo-sensitive materials, a point entirely missed in the original brief. Modifications were made and a cover provided. The project was made even more difficult by the discovery that termites had eaten the original set of drawings. A new lot had to be drawn.

Steam technology is still very important in India. Nozzle testing apparatus was designed for production in the Centre's workshops. It was designed to use as many standard components as possible, including bits of bicycle chain wheel as well as steam valves and gauges. The original one was difficult to monitor, as the gauges, valves and condensers were all over the front, back and sides.

In the redesigned unit all the controls requiring monitoring were brought to the front of the machine. Simple value analysis enabled components, that had originally been left or right handed castings, to be designed as standard castings simply machined to left or right. The frames were designed to afford some protection during transport, either by rail or more usually by bullock cart.

Other projects included such items as a fabric laminating press; a Michelson Interferometer and an Angle Dekkor, together with various graphic projects.

Our work at IIT(D) has left us sceptical of the value of conventional aid either in the form of hardware, as a direct gift or as a license to manufacture. These processes only allow limited experience to be gained, rather than the wealth of experience that can be built up from designing and manufacturing a product from scratch, suitable for the rigours of use in India. On the positive side, the programme at IIT(D) left behind a design method and evidence of practice. Design is now part of undergraduate engineering education there, and a limited number of items did go into actual production financed by indigenous entrepreneurs. We believe the programme was a reasonably cost-effective means by which the UK government provided aid in answer to a need raised by the Institute of Technology itself.

SOCIAL FORCES DETERMINE THE SHAPE OF TECHNOLOGY
Thomas Kuby

Roughly half of the fifty-three papers announced for this symposium indicate by their title that they deal with some kind of technological innovation, be it the design of disaster equipment or the conception of an eco-house. I would like to draw your attention to some aspects of design which, in one way or another, are linked to concepts of an intermediate, alternative or appropriate technology. If such a considerable part of Design for Need activities relies on a new technological input, it is certainly necessary to be much clearer than we are at present about the chances of bettering situations of need by changing the technological factors which define them.

In his book 'Small is Beautiful' Schumacher writes:

> 'I believe ... that the best way to make contact with the essen-
> tial problem is by speaking of technology. Economic develop-
> ment in poverty-stricken areas can be fruitful only on the
> basis of what I have called "intermediate technology" ... a
> different kind of technology, a technology with a human face
> which, instead of making human hands and brains redundant
> helps them to become far more productive than they have
> ever been before. ' (p 168/154)

The argument that a change in technology is required if we are to do away with need and poverty is compelling, and in a way it is very materialistic. History tells us that the steam engine, the Bessemer converter, the typewriter, the radio and the motor car all greatly changed social structures and, of course, there can be no doubt that technological changes influence, and even radically change, the life and work of large groups of people. In fact, the greater part of the history of technology is based on a concept of 'social lag', which holds that technology changes society by changing its living and working conditions, to which society then has to adapt; the time between technological change and social adaptation is called 'social lag'.

With much of Schumacher's argument one is bound to agree. He is right, I believe, in saying that scientific knowledge allows many different technological applications, which open up a wide choice of technologies. Likewise, it seems rational to assume that the widespread existence and use of an alternative technology would do much to ease the solution of many development problems we are faced with today. In fact, the argument is so persuasive that one wonders why we do not have a more rational technology, with which we would all be better off. Are we to assume that some technological alternatives are being suppressed? And if this is so, what forces determine the direction of technological progress?

According to Schumacher, we are faced with an 'insurmountable bias in favour of

large scale projects on the level of the most modern technology'. At the same time,
those working on alternative technology projects

> 'do not know of one another, do not support one another, and
> cannot be of assistance to those who want to follow a similar
> road but do not know how to get started. They exist, as it
> were, outside the mainstream of official and popular interest. '
> (p 177)

Schumacher therefore proposes that we come together, pool all our knowledge and
experience, and at the same time use all our influence to 'turn official and popular
interest away from the grandiose projects'. 'I have no doubts' he writes 'that it is
possible to give a new direction to technological development ... to redirect
technology primarily requires an effort of the imagination and an abandonment of fear'.

I am not at all sure that changing technology is as simple as this. I suspect that
Schumacher idealistically underestimates the true complexity of technological
innovation. Historical analysis, as well as experience with alternative technology
projects, suggests that the shape of existing technology is determined by very powerful forces which cannot be overcome simply by personal will and ability. One of the
best ways to identify these forces is to look into history and to analyse distinctive
'shapes of technology' in the past.

An outstanding example of the emergence of a distinctly different technology is given
by the so-called 'American system' of manufacture which gained prominence in the
first half of the 19th century, and stunned British industrialists for its lightness,
efficiency, ingenuity and economy.

The machines differed from sturdy Victorian designs, especially in raw-material and
energy consumption, complexity and productivity. Their design was consumer
oriented allowing a much more decentralised pattern of production. Their products
were characterised by standardisation, simplicity and interchangeability of parts.
In all these respects they showed the distinctive 'shape of technology'.

Whilst Burlingame and Habakkuk attribute the development of the new production
system to the lack of trained mechanics, Peter Temmin (in his famous controversy
with Habakkuk) concludes that high interest rates were mainly responsible. George
Daniels who considers this the 'Big Question in the History of American Technology'
(title of his book) argues in his important essay on the 'American System' that all
these explanations, although pointing to a social cause of technological change, still
fall far short of the real degree of complexity. Some of the social forces that Daniels
sees at work in early America are; a democratic educational system, social flexibility,
the absence of rigid classes or professions, a high degree of freedom in choice of
work, high social regard for material success and a firm belief in the moral necessity
to raise productivity. The optimistic climate of an expanding society goes a long way
in explaining the lack of worker opposition to labour-saving machinery. (This is very
much in contrast to conditions in England where Abraham Colt failed to set up a rifle
factory in Pimlico because the workers would not have it.)

These same features (of a progressive capitalist society) account for the quick exchange of information among American producers and thus for the astonishing speed and breadth of technological progress. Puritan heritage, a simple 'frontier life', the special conditions of colonisation of the American continent by the white man (with light rifles from the back of a horse in a vast country where you had to be able to 'gut a gun', ie make one new one from two broken ones made with exchangeable parts) and a strong preference for simple and practical things - all these were decisive social factors which both anticipated and supported an American system of machinery for standardised mass-production. Daniels concludes:

> 'Technology is being used to help people to do things better
> which they have already been doing for other reasons - and
> what they were doing for other reasons determines the
> character of their future technology. '

If this argument is slightly one-sided it none the less leads to a general conclusion. All the factors mentioned by Daniels relate more or less directly to the relations of production, which exist between producers irrespective of their personal ambitions. The relations described by Daniels characterise a capitalist society in its progressive, revolutionary phase where the development of the forces of production is extremely fast and shows a high degree of 'appropriateness', ie of correlation with the specific needs and possibilities of society. The general conclusion seems to be that there exists indeed a strong link between the relations of production and the forces of production and that primarily technology is not a cause, but an effect of social forces which determine its shape.

An example of intermediate technology development work may further illustrate this understanding of technological innovation. The Intermediate Technology Development Group (ITDG) 'egg-tray machine' is frequently cited as a successful example of an alternative technological approach. However, I would argue that in fact it is much more an example of the failure of this approach. Of course, as an isolated bit of machinery, the egg-tray machine can be called successful: it worked and it was even 'economically viable' - both rather against the expectations of the experts. But technology is, if anything, a means for people to develop their potentials, which in this particular case meant the abolition of very severe forms of poverty. Measured in this way, the egg-tray machine is less successful, although as an example it is very instructive.

The prototype version of the machine, developed at Reading University and the Royal College of Art, fulfilled four requirements which Schumacher lists as guidelines for intermediate technology development work:

> Because of its simple design, its relatively low energy
> consumption and its division into functional segments which
> could be handled without a crane, the machine was well suited
> for operation in rural regions of poor countries. It created
> work places where the people are living and not in the
> metropolitan areas into which they tend to migrate.

The machine was cheap and therefore the work places it
created were cheap. Built in England in 1972 the cost price
of the machine was less than £6,000 and without the electric
dryer (which had been built for test purposes in England but
was not needed in most African countries) the cost price of
the machine fell to less than £4,000. Four work places were
directly linked to the operation of the machine but many more
were created indirectly by the simple fact that something
useful was produced in an area where nothing of this sort was
produced before.

The production methods were simple. With the work process
organised on an hourly rotation scheme which reduced
competition and hierarchy the workers were in a position to
learn to run the plant themselves without a superimposed
technical management. Job-rotation minimised the division
of labour and thus prevented the work from becoming an
'inhuman chore'.

The product was for local use (agriculture packaging) and made
from locally available raw material (waste paper).

When in 1972 a prototype version of this machine proved technically reliable ITDG
made arrangements for its production by a factory in the Midlands and started to
offer it to several developing countries through intermediate technology channels.
The last sentence of the ITDG offer read: 'We are constantly improving this plant in
the light of further demands and all figures and sizes quoted are subject to modification
according to local conditions. ' It looks a sensible proposition to make, but in fact
it turned out as a programme of redesign of that machine to suit the prevailing social,
political and economic conditions.

Original plans to supply the first factory-made machines to Zambian or Tanzanian
agricultural co-operatives did not materialise because of local problems. ITDG
therefore sold the first three machines to the Military District Government of Enugu
in Nigeria. A fourth plant was delivered to a private business-man in Accra. His,
as well as the Military Government's requirements proved to be rather different from
those which had guided the design process and the building of the prototype. Consequently a number of decisive technical characteristics of the plant were altered. The
first plants produced for sale included the electric dryer which greatly reduced the
possibility of operating the plant in rural areas. Instead of air-drying the trays in
locally produced shelves as had been planned the new customers did not want to
burden themselves with the task of building parts of the plant in their own country;
they wanted to buy the 'whole package' shipped directly from England to the site
where the plant was to operate. Since they intended to operate the plant in metropolitan areas where cranes were available they saw of course no point in segmenting
the service station into functional, lightweight parts; this part of the machine therefore
was built in one. Instead of using two forming stations - which doubled the plant's
capacity at 25% additional cost - the plant was to have only one forming station but
with a 20% increased output. This kind of scaling up of the plant's capacity was
completely against its design intentions and had two detrimental effects. On the one

hand the next larger size of pumps and driving motors had to be used which meant an over-proportionate boost of energy consumption and a further reduction in rural applicability. This would have been avoided if instead of increasing peak-loads the duration of an average load had been spread by using a second forming station. The twenty per cent capacity increase on the other hand meant a reduction of the cycle time of the forming station to its technical minimum of twenty seconds which left the worker no room for a rest pause and made his work very exhausting and intensive. The reduction of cycle time would have been possible with fewer detrimental effects upon the worker if the forming station had been equipped with a simple compressed-air mechanism to operate the swing-motion of the mould, but no use was made of this option in the first machines. Needless to say, no attention was given to job-rotation and team co-operation with the effect that the workers were hierarchically split by different work requirements and instead of collectively mastering their means of production they were treated as, and became, a mere addition to the machine. Since they had no interest in their work but only in the money they could earn through their work, a special technical manager was required to look after the equipment. Accordingly the plant was supplied by ITDG with a device to count the number of production cycles in order to prevent pilfering.

The end of the story must be related to its beginning. In 1970 when ITDG decided to develop an egg-tray machine the smallest machine on the market had a capacity of 1.3 million trays per year and cost roughly £120,000. The machine was fully automatic and required only one highly qualified operator. The machine was inadequate for creating work places in the rural areas of poor countries. ITDG therefore set out to develop an intermediate alternative and in technical terms it succeeded. Step by step, however, the 'alternative' character of the new technology has been eroded. Today a Mark III version of the egg-tray machine is being built which is said to produce more than two million trays per year and to cost £100,000. Scale, output and price being about the same, the intermediate technology concept shrinks to a cynical proposition to offer the poor countries of the world a primitive, labour-intensive technology which has most of the disadvantages of large scale while lacking all the positive sides of modern technology and automation. The story seems to have gone full circle but it isn't even back to where it started.

The conclusions one seems bound to draw from this historical analysis of technological innovation and from experience with developing alternative technology have, I believe, far-reaching and important consequences for any concept of Design for Need. Although occasionally and against terrific odds, alternative structures emerge, their proliferation and widespread use is blocked by strong social, political and economic forces which shape the existing technology. Hence, alternative projects are bound to either collapse or to adapt. There is little ground for assuming that alternative technologies can grow to such strength that they indeed begin to change social conditions instead of being diluted, absorbed and disposed by them. Inevitably therefore, Design for Need is up against politics. It is not just another job which you do as a designer; you can't spend seven hours of a working day designing for want and then another hour designing for need. Design for Need, I would argue, is possible only as a 'strategy of conflict' with the designers themselves acutely aware of the political implications of their work. Design for Need must politically side with the poor and the underprivileged or else it will fail. It is, as Schumacher writes; 'basically a problem of compassion with the ordinary people of the world'. I could not agree more, because only the 'ordinary people', the workers and peasants in both rich and poor countries, will in the end be capable of changing those social, political and economic forces which today suppress a more rational use of our intellectual and material resources. And only in contact with people rather than books will the engineer or designer learn to apply what he has learned from books for a 'better human environment'.

THE NEED FOR DESIGN EDUCATION
IN DEVELOPING COUNTRIES
Alphonso Gomez

At a time when technological and cultural innovation seem necessary in order to
keep pace with the social challenges which markedly characterise our age, the
recognition of the full potential of Design does not only call for a change in Design,
but most importantly it suggests that social change can be achieved by Design.

If one analyses the various definitions of Design, it becomes apparent that the
characteristics which are attributed to this activity vary a great deal according to
the interests and background of the people who invent such definitions. This means
that Design is not 'socially neutral', but an activity which influences and is influenced
by the balance of interests between the different social groups which participate in
the design process (mainly producer, user and designer). Design is not merely an
activity dealing with objects or abstract systems, but is primarily a vehicle for
social interaction.

Let us next centre our attention on the implications of the term 'Development'.
Modern history tells us how difficult it is to agree as to what constitutes socio-
economic development and how to achieve it. There is one point though which finds
virtually universal consensus: underdevelopment is probably the worst, most dangerous and most widespread of contemporary social 'diseases'. But the essential
issue remains to be clarified: what should be the target of socio-economic development?
Or in other words, when can we say that a society is a developed one?

According to some, a country is underdeveloped if it has average annual earnings of
less than $600 US per capita (1). A simple figure like this gives us hardly more than
a rough division between the economic output of rich and poor nations. There is good
reason to be highly suspicious of these purely economic approaches.

There seems to be a problem with the very term 'Development', which stems from a
kind of intrinsic positivism that the term carries with it. But even the most optimistic
studies recognise that, without the intervention of serious changes in the organisation
of society, there will be no decent housing for the great majority of coming generations,
no adequate health service, no adequate education, most probably not even enough
food. The trends in economic growth very clearly show that the gap between rich and
poor is increasing.

What constitutes a 'developed society' is not a group of absolute economic or social
indicants in isolation. Societies are only developed or underdeveloped with respect
to each other. In this sense it can be argued that the only economies which deserve
the denomination 'developing' are those of already high standards of living and that
the poorer nations should rather be referred to as 'underdeveloping'.

Ready acceptance by the Third World of the rich nations' understanding of the term Development has at least two serious implications. First it would mean to subjugate the goals and objectives of the process of socio-economic development to those already existing in the industrialised nations. This implies not only surrendering cultural identity but it also means being forced to inherit many of the undesirable side-effects of contemporary technology, such as depletion of resources, ecological disharmony etc. Secondly it can be said that such an attitude sets, for the Third World, a kind of utopia or illusory target; that is, a situation in which the objectives of Development seem more remote all the time.

The concept of Underdevelopment cannot be separated from the idea of cultural and economic dependence. Dependence is not a term opposed to underdevelopment, but actually one which embraces it and helps to define the goals of Development in a more desirable way. Rather than relying on purely numeric parameters, Development is expressed in this case as a degree of socio-economic independence. Underdevelopment can also be seen as a particular state of mind or a form of awareness. Illich sees this aspect as 'an extreme result of what can be called in the language of both Marx and Freud, "Verdinglichung", that is, reification'(2). (That is the conversion of a person or an abstract concept into a material thing. In this case it is used in the sense of hardening the perception of real needs into the demands for mass manufactured products. Illich illustrates this as 'the translation of thirst into the need for a coke'.)

Designing for the needy is often interpreted by well meaning designers of industrial economies as an opportunity to redeem themselves from the sin of consumer orientation. The risk contained in such action is that it can easily fall either into the 'trivial' or even worse, into the 'folksy'.

In the case of the 'trivial', 'need' is interpreted as something on the lines of 'that without which physiological life can hardly take place'. The only subjects which are accepted as being socially responsible (and therefore worthy of Design) are, in this view, the rather typical collection of graphic aids for the illiterate, emergency shelter, aids for the disabled etc. But how about other less 'respectable' kinds of objects such as chairs, hair-driers or products for leisure? Should the underdeveloped ever have access to this type of goods, or should we designers 'save' them from expressing their needs so wrongly?

The 'folksy' approach is in its turn characterised by a rather narrow attitude towards culture, by which designers seek to glorify some colourful but rather fossilised aspects of culture in a commonly naive way. Mistaken paternalism is a common factor in either of these views.

Although there is a great deal to be learned from the design experience of industrialised nations, a willingness to search for a kind of libertarian and controllable innovation must be generated basically from within the dependent society, at all levels of its organisation. It is here that the potential role of design education becomes apparent. For the need for design in developing countries consists basically of incorporating design education effectively into the struggle for cultural and economic independence - a term used here not in a narrow chauvinistic sense, but meaning a fairer kind of interdependence between richer and poorer nations.

Although it is argued that a reformulation of the goals and structures of contemporary society (developing countries in particular) is badly needed, there is a socially responsible role for the designer in developing nations at this very moment. The basis for such a role is design education, not only for the specialist designer (as in the case of traditional industrial design schools) but for all the agencies intervening in design. The traditional school of industrial design is an 'under-dimensioned' institution when a contribution to national socio-economic development is set out as the ultimate goal.

The fundamental new task that the equivalent to design schools should undertake in the developing economies, is that of expanding its responsibility from the mere training of designer, to raising the level of design awareness among users, producers and authorities. Under this scheme, traditional lectures, seminars etc are only a small proportion of the activities which are called for. The setting up of research programmes, extensive use of mass communication media, production of guides for design discrimination, circulation of papers putting forward a case for technological innovation and explaining its potential value for local industry etc are just a few examples of the tasks which could be undertaken. A concentrated dose of will, imagination and intelligence should determine what to do exactly in each specific case.

The part that professional designers are expected to undertake in this strategy becomes necessarily expanded. The few designers that a developing society can afford should be infinitely more than just experts in ergonomics, aesthetics, industrial processes etc, they should be the main catalysts in the new role which is being advocated here for Design.

I firmly believe that all this, plus a reappraisal of the relations between design agencies of developed and underdeveloped worlds, should establish a firm basis for a significant contribution of design education to the cultural and economic liberation of the poorer nations. If these words sound a bit too grand it might be worthwhile reminding ourselves that while no men are completely free, there is little doubt that as the result of underdevelopment, some of them are freer than others.

REFERENCES

A Gomez, A Contribution to Curriculum Development in Design Education (Royal College of Art, London 1975)

(1) G Jones, The Role of Science and Technology in Developing Countries (Oxford University Press 1971)

D Freire, Cultural Action for Freedom (Penguin 1971)

(2) I Illich, Planned Poverty: The End Result of Technical Assistance (from In Celebration of Awareness, Penguin 1971)

V Papanek & others, Third World Cautions (Design magazine No 332)

DESHANAGARI: A COMMON SCRIPT FOR ALL INDIAN LANGUAGES
Raghunath Krishna Joshi

A major challenge to people in the field of communication in India today is to find an effective means of coping with the ever-increasing demands for faster and more efficient modes of communication while fostering the rare multilingual character of our country. In mass education and adult literacy, science and technology, these demands are particularly urgent.

Normally, one language and one script would be ideal for efficient communication. However, our many well-developed languages have a deep-rooted and overlapping influence on the cultural environment. The task of evolving one script, then becomes more complex. On a national scale, this acquires an even more significant dimension. It is imperative therefore that, in the interest of covering all the areas of national discipline, a unifying element be established - an auxiliary script which serves as the link script for all the Indian languages.

Deshanagari is the name given to the proposed common script, which is an extension of Devanagari. (Devanagari was chosen as the base script because it is the most widely used Indian script in existence today, and it bears a close structural relationship to the majority of Indian scripts.) Deshanagari differs from Devanagari in two respects:

> A few structural changes in the script help to overcome the graphic and sequential defects of Devanagari, so that different forms of application, manual or mechanical, are made easier.

> Deshanagari has extra letter signs as against Devanagari. It can therefore be used for any phonetic transcriptions from any Indian language.

The Deshanagari system consists of twenty-two vowel letter signs and fifty-two consonant letter signs - a comprehensive range with which it is possible to write any message in any Indian language. In other words, it will serve as a common script for our country - Desh. Hence it is called Desh-anagari.

Salient Features of Deshanagari and their Advantages

> 1 A visual resemblance between vowels and their corresponding vowel signs is achieved. For instance, the vowel इ in Devanagari has the vowel sign ि . In Deshanagari the sign ह has been used as a vowel letter sign, to achieve a total resemblance between vowel and vowel sign. This

42

resemblance makes for easier recognition and quicker association of the vowel with its sound. Learning the infrastructure of the script is made easier. The repetition of visual symbols helps to build up confidence in a child or a beginner.

2 In Deshanagari, the vowel letter sign is merely added to a consonant letter sign, which is always a half-consonant.

CONSONANT   VOWEL
LETTER SIGN   LETTER SIGN

$$\text{ᘯ} + \text{ᘰ} = \text{ᘯᘰ}$$

The visual association of vowel letter sign and sound added to half-consonant is sustained throughout.

3 All the vowel letter signs join the consonant letter signs only at one place, on the right; following the linear method.

DEVANAGARI   के   DESHANAGARI   ᘯᘰ

BENGLI   কে   DESHANAGARI   ᘯᘰ

GUJARATHI   કે   DESHANAGARI   ᘯᘰ

Standardising the one-place attachment will quicken the process of learning, particularly for those not familiar with the script and for the illiterate.

4 In Deshanagari conjuncts, half and full consonants appear in their correct form. Consistent conjunct formulation is achieved.

DEVANAGARI   DESHANAGARI

व्य = व् + य   c + य = cय
ड्य = ड् + य   ड + य = ड्य
क्व = क् + व   क + व = क्व

5 Word-formation in Deshanagari has an identical phonetic and graphic sequence, providing a consistent relationship between sound and sign.

DEVANAGARI   मूर्ति = म् + ऊ + इ + त + र्
                      1   2   5   4   3

DESHANAGARI   ᘯᘰᘱᘲ = म् + ऊ + र् + त् + इ
                    = म् + ऊ + र् + त् + इ
                      1   2   3   4   5

6 A two-tier structure is achieved. This will make the body of
the letter bigger in any given size of type. On the one hand
it makes reading easier, on the other it also overcomes many
of the drawbacks confronted by Devanagari - eg in relation to
size of type; in printing technology.

DEVANAGARI   DESHANAGARI

7 Signs such as 'halant', 'nukta', the crescent mark and 'anuswara'
have all been placed in a sequential order and position in
relation to the letters.

Halant (ॖ) DEVA कट्टा DESH कटटी

The revised placement of the halant sign (ie after the letter,
placed horizontally) helps the reader connect the letter logically
and pronounce the word correctly.

Nukta (·) URDU   DESH -પમસल

Used at its most functional, before the letter, in the upper half,
the nukta guides the reader into the correct pronunciation. Thus,
one sign - a mere dot - also suggests the various possibilities
of pronunciation, making it very economical in its multilingual
application. The double nukta is used to indicate implosives.

SINDHI   DESH ··ୟ

Crescent mark (◡) HINDI हँसना DESH हा6सना

Made linear, the crescent and the nasal crescent mark have
a better calligraphic flow, and contribute to speedier writing.

The anuswara (०) DEVA सिंह DESHA ४हु०੮

For the anuswara, the linear device used in other Indian scripts
(ie Malayalam, Kannada, Bengali, etc) has been adopted.

8 The overspread forms of some letters as they exist in Devanagari
have been simplified and changed. This will increase legibility
and will help to construct all the letters within a minimum grid.

DEVA   DESH   DEVA   DESH

ह्   ९   छ्   ఆ

9 When vowel 'a' is added, all consonants end with a vertical
stroke.

DEVANAGARI   DESHANAGARI

क् + अ = क   द् + | = द|

फ् + अ = फ   प् + | = प|

The half-forms of certain consonants are achieved by shifting
the halant in a linear manner, as shown in item 7.

The half-forms of certain consonants.

To this half-form, the addition of vertical stroke 'a' is a
logical sequel.

10 Extra vowels and consonants have been added to cover most
of the pronunciations of the major Indian languages. These
will make it possible to render phonetically and visually in
Deshanagari, all the sounds in all the languages.

11 Numerals: the universally used Arabic numerals will be
retained in Deshanagari.

12 Over 2,000 combinations are possible from the 22 vowel
letter signs and 52 consonant letter signs in Deshanagari.
These can function within a sign list of 80 types (vowel and
relevant signs-18; half-consonants-37; numerals-10; and
essential signs-15).

DESHANAGARI

VOWEL LETTER SIGNS 22

CONSONANT LETTER SIGNS 52

DEVA

IPA

VOWEL LETTER SIGNS→DESH
CONSONANT LETTER SIGNS↓
DEVA   IPA DESH

DESHANAGARI SIGN LIST : 80 (18 VOWEL LETTER SIGN, 37 CONSONANT LETTER SIGNS
15 ESSENTIAL OTHER SIGNS 10 NUMERAL SIGNS)

1	2	3	4	5	6	7	8	9	10	11	12	13	14	15	16

COMBINATIONS OF CONSONANT LETTER SIGN k AND VOWEL LETTER SIGNS

Kə   Kə: Ka   Ka: Ki   Ki: Ku   Ku: Kɨ

Kɨ: Krɨ   Ke   Ke: Kæ   Kəi   Ko   Ko: Kɔ

Kəu   KəN   KəH   K

COMBINATIONS OF CONSONANT LETTER SIGN k AND OTHER CONSONANT LETTER SIGNS

Klə: KKə: Kvə: Knə: Krə: rkə: Ktrə: Ktə:

Practical Applications and Scope for Development

Deshanagari offers immense scope in long-term uses. These fall into three broad
categories:

Education

a) Learning different Indian languages becomes easier. The
student who attempts an unfamiliar language does not have
to go through the whole process of learning its equally
unfamiliar script.

b) In other fields, both professional and academic, the advantages
of Deshanagari as a common script are significant. For
example, in journalism - a reporter could use any language
but just one script. In translation and interpretation too,
operations are simplified. The production of research
material and books of academic interest is also made easier
(eg dictionaries, grammars, etc).

Technology

a) The various forms of printing technology will benefit
considerably with the use of a common script. Mechanical
typesetting machines (such as Linotype or Monotype) would
be used more extensively in India as well as more advanced
composing machines (typositors, for example). An obvious
advantage in typewriters is the fact that the 'dead' keys now on
the Devanagari typewriter would be eliminated, enhancing typing
speed. A further possibility is the bilingual typewriter, with
the keyboard in Deshanagari and the types in another script.
This would enable the transfer of an entire message from the
common script into the regional language.

b) As a base for mechanisation, Deshanagari has specific
advantages: telephone and other signalling codes, computer
codes, optical character reading equipment, teleprinters -
all acquire a common script shared by sixteen languages.

Communication

a) For persuasive communication, one script would ease many of
the mechanical problems in execution. In organisations
where many languages are used simultaneously, Deshanagari
would help to speed up work - eg (at the applied level) Films
Division, All India Radio, central libraries, etc and (at the
academic level) research institutes, where parallel studies
of different languages are carried out.

b) Interstate communication at government levels would be more
economical. All stationery forms, etc and all publications
and printed matter for common use (eg reports of committees,
census findings, etc) could be printed in Deshanagari.

c) Environmental communication - the rendering of names all
over India would be standardised with the use of the Deshanagari
script. From a telephone directory - which could be printed
in the language of the State and in the common script of the
country - to sign boards, maps, all forms of railway signage,
bus stops, street names. The possibilities are endless.

Project Deshanagari - a summary of the work in hand

The basic work of evolving a sign list for Deshanagari is completed (notes and relevant
charts are under preparation). Though it has been broadly checked for its compre-
hensiveness, it needs further detailed analysis so that the final recommended sign
list will be thoroughly comprehensive and practical.

Schemes for adult education, using Deshanagari, are to be developed. The target
group includes those who write Devanagari or any other script, neo-literates and
illiterates.

In children's books, the possibility of combining pictograms and Deshanagari has to
be explored. Depending on the requirements of the educationists, this could develop
in several directions: from a pictoral multilingual dictionary, to simultaneous teaching
of more than one language, right from the primary level.

Sample pages of bilingual dictionaries and grammar using Deshanagari have been
worked out but further development is needed in the area of publishing reading material
in different languages, using one script. (A parallel example would be tourist folders
in Switzerland).

Development in the area of printing technology is presently under consideration. A
typeface in Deshanagari has to be designed and cast for hand composing. The
adaptation of the Deshanagari sign list to suit mechanical typesetting machines (such
as Protype, Linotype, Monotype) and typewriter/teleprinter is already planned, however
the correct layouts of the respective keyboards are yet to be designed. The case for
the Deshanagari bilingual typewriter for interstate communication also has to be carefully studied. For mechanical writing by computer: the simplified version of letters
and their grid has to be developed. Likewise, the scope for using Deshanagari in
written messages on television has to be worked out.

To evaluate the following aspects of Deshanagari, sample studies are to be undertaken:

> Constructional changes in graphems
> Form simplification
> Processes of word formation/recognition

The studies would cover

Children   at the pre-primary stage (whose mother tongue is Hindi/Marathi)
at the primary level (whose mother tongue is Hindi/Marathi)
at the secondary school level (with any mother tongue)

Adults   Literates (whose mother tongue is Hindi/Marathi)
              Literates (with any mother tongue other than the above)
              Illiterates (speaking any language)

The information obtained from these sample studies would be invaluable, and once
incorporated into the Deshanagari system, it would be ready for application.

The Place of Deshanagari in the Linguascriptic Pattern of India

In its initial stage, Deshanagari will not replace any existing script nor is it devised
to be attached to any language as a part of it - it will be treated as an auxiliary script
to be taught/learnt as a means for quicker and more efficient multilingual exchange
at all levels of national interest. It will represent Indian writing on the international
scene (alongside Chinese, Russian etc).

For communication within the State, the use of regional scripts and languages will
continue.   Literature in different languages will be printed in their own script, but
to make it accessible to people speaking other languages it will also be printed in
Deshanagari, whenever needed.

If it is found to be more convenient, Deshanagari will replace Devanagari in future -
a transition that can be smoothly made because of their relation. (Deshanagari texts
can be composed, for printing purposes, with only a minor addition of a few types
in Devanagari.)

In Devanagari areas, it will be easy for children and adults to learn the Deshanagari
system. In non-Devanagari areas, children will be exposed to Deshanagari only
after learning the regional script, and adults whose working area requires a multilingual
exchange will learn Deshanagari as an additional script.

All illiterates in this country will be exposed to Deshanagari - they will be speaking
different languages but will write only one script, thereby facilitating the co-ordination
and the extensive spread of literacy schemes throughout the country. For neo-literates
one script will expedite programmes already planned, in terms of printing technical
terms and/or relevant information in connection with their subject in functional
literacy.

To sum up, Deshanagari - the common script - will exist without interfering with the
present linguascriptic pattern of our country. At the same time it will make a positive
contribution in the areas where a multilingual exchange is important for national
integration. For the new generation of children and neo-literates Deshanagari should
prove to be the vital need of the time.

CERAMICS FOR THE DEVELOPING WORLD

*Prof. Lord Queensberry, Abdul Gaffoor
and Lynne Reeve*

The ceramic industries of developing countries should be in contrast to the sophisticated industries of countries like Germany, Japan, USA and the UK which have evolved
over the years to:

> Reduce the labour content, using machines with high production
> speeds requiring skilled design and maintenance but only semi-
> skilled operatives.

> Foster belief in an absolutely uniform and predictable product
> in which any irregularity is seen as a fault.

> Develop more and more complicated decorating processes
> whereby designs conceived on the flat can be applied to the
> compound curvature of ceramic shapes (relying in turn on a
> secondary industry producing transfers).

> Rely more and more on the half dozen suppliers of ceramic
> materials; glazes, colours, stains, frits,etc.

But these are all developments that a developing country can do without. For them,
labour intensive production is better than capital intensive automated plants. As
they can never produce the uniformity developed over many years in the ceramic
centres of the world (Nagoya, Stoke on Trent, Limoges etc), they are surely better off
not striving for this spurious concept of quality. They have people who can be trained
to decorate using simple manual techniques now abandoned by the 'sophisticated'
industries. (The idea of using ceramic transfers in India for instance is absurd.)
Likewise, ceramic materials that will make perfectly acceptable bodies and glazes
exist virtually everywhere. It should be possible to formulate satisfactory products
from existing raw materials so as to be independent of the large suppliers of
ceramic products. But ironically the industry still relies on imports. For example
a ceramic plant has been set up in an undeveloped part of Canada to manufacture
ceramic tableware from a basic body imported with twenty-four per cent moisture
content from Stoke on Trent. The plant however, is no more than thirty miles from
a deposit of red-burning secondary clay, which could make a very satisfactory and
extremely attractive ceramic body, preferable by most people's standards to the
imported material.

Three projects at the Royal College of Art provide more encouraging examples.
First: a project in which the Royal College of Art has been deeply involved, Scottish
Highland Stoneware. David Grant has set up a stoneware factory in the Highlands of
Scotland, where it has been possible, with very small capital investment, to produce
a remarkably competitive product. The viability of the unit depends on:

A product that differs from the monotonous and lifeless products
of large-scale industry.

The use of simple decorative techniques that contemporary
industry has forgotten.

The purchase of amazingly cheap equipment that sophisticated
industry considers obsolete.

Excellent local raw materials, in particular the felspatic
rock which, with a small addition of clay, makes a perfect
and predictable stoneware glaze.

The valuable loans and grants that are available in developing
areas (not only in the UK).

A second project (featured in a recent ITDG journal) is a man-powered jolly developed
by Abdul Gaffoor. The jolly works like a potters wheel with a mould that is rotated on
a vertical axis. A slug of clay is thrown into the mould and a tool is brought down into
the mould forming a vessel between the static tool and the rotating mould. Until
recently this was the established method to make cups and bowls but it has always
used an external power source, normally an electric motor. In Abdul Gaffoor's
design the operative supplies the power by kicking a crank, the method that is often
used to turn the potter's wheel. The adaptation can be made with the simplest
materials available almost anywhere in the world. Learning to throw competently on
a potter's wheel can take years and many people fail, however a jolly does not require
anything like the same skill. A less skilled person with only a few months training
could achieve a better rate of production than is possible by throwing.

The third example is the binary testing of materials for ceramic glazes: a project by
a research student, Lynne Reeve. Most traditional pottery glazes are made from five
or six minerals, each (with its own melting point) contributing a different surface
quality or colour to the glaze. It is difficult to examine the behaviour of any single
ingredient when used with a large number of other materials, especially since the
properties of the finished glaze are often due to the effects of combinations of minerals.

The research is limited to simple two-ingredient recipes. Approximately thirty
materials are thus tested in all possible pairs (given of course that silicon, the
essential glass forming element is present). For each pair eleven different glazes
are prepared ranging from 100% of material A, to 100% material B, in 10% steps.

Similar studies have doubtless been made before. In fact some of the experimental
results strongly suggest a link with techniques of the distant past. But today such
basic data is either unavailable or is bypassed by more sophisticated testing and
calculation methods restricted to modern industry's traditional compositions.

The data is of potential value in several areas:

Supplies of certain minerals which the ceramic industry
is used to are running out; others are becoming scarce
and expensive; an increasing number are regarded as toxic.

However the research demonstrates that certain materials
are more versatile than current practice suggest. A basic
knowledge of the materials will enable the glaze technologist
to make substitutions.

The work also shows the effect of what would normally be
regarded as excessively large quantities of material in certain
glazes. Such knowledge will be of use where specific materials
occur naturally in abundance.

The firing temperatures of glazes fall roughly in two categories:
stoneware glazes fired at $125^{\circ}C$ or over; or earthenware fired
between $1,000^{\circ}$ and $1,150^{\circ}C$. Many minerals melt at the
higher temperature but this clearly requires larger amounts
of fuel. The earthenware glazes almost always involve the
use of prefired frits. The research will pinpoint the lowest
temperature at which glazes can be made from naturally
occurring minerals without the use of frits, thereby suggesting
glazes that require the minimum thermal energy.

The work is sponsored by the Crafts Advisory Council and the results will be published.
Although this is a craft-based study the basic nature of the information makes it
relevant to anyone involved in the manufacture of essential ceramic goods where
technology is at a minimum and raw materials at a premium.

THE ROLE OF THE DESIGNER IN DISASTER RELIEF
Dr. John Murlis

Over the years since the last world war, and particularly since the Nigerian Civil
War, there has been an increase in public interest in disaster relief. This is reflect
in the growth of relief agencies like Oxfam or Save the Children Fund, the non-
government agencies and in the formation of UNDRO (the United Nations Disaster
Relief Organisation). Together these organisations spend a vast sum of money each
year on materials and equipment and it is quite natural, therefore, that designers
should become concerned with their activities. But what exactly is it that a designer
can contribute? Although this may seem self-evident, experience shows that contributions to disaster design are often ineffective or do not address themselves to real
needs. What I wish to do here is to examine the role of designers in disaster relief
by analysing past design effort and by attempting to define principles in the light of
previous experience.

THE PRESSURE ENVIRONMENT OF THE AGENCIES

Relief agencies are heavily dependent upon public response to appeals for funding of
disaster relief. They are therefore very aware of their public image and the fact tha
this is largely determined by the press: adverse reporting of an operation can be fata
to an agency's credibility. Furthermore the press plays an important role in determining activities' since agencies feel under pressure to react to reported disasters a
may do so on the basis of press reports. But the press/public cycle forms only a par
of the pressure environment in which the agencies operate. There is also pressure
from the community of 'experts' in all disciplines (but mainly in medical and economi
sciences) and from industry, commerce and other categories of people with goods or
services for sale. These two 'pressure bodies', like the press, deal in information I
their kinds of information are very different in nature and quality. The press has, o
necessity, a very simplified view of disaster and needs to hold the interest of reader
and so it gives emphasis to the dramatic, rather than to the commonplace acts which
are sensible but uninteresting. In complete contrast the kinds of information provide
by experts are very detailed and may contain an analytical framework and conclusion
of some complexity. Although the quality of information may be high, there is a high
possibility of misinterpretation - thus information going from relief operators to
experts, follows an impeded or broken path to relief agencies.

Commercial and industrial concerns, in contrast have very simple kinds of informati
stemming from a very proper belief in their ability to contribute to relief operations,
and it must be said now that many concerns involved in disaster relief have altruistic
motives. Unfortunately the products and services involved have developed, in genera
in circumstances quite different from those of a disaster and may therefore depend or
mis-information about disasters, whatever the intentions of their creators. The
communication between this pressure group and the relief agencies is fairly straight-

forward, firstly because it is intrinsically simple but also because it concerns tangibles rather than ideas.

There is some evidence that relief agencies are aware of these pressures and are developing means of dealing at least with the funding, for example by advertising their activities and by school visiting. In the past, however, being under pressure to solve a particular problem apparently dominating relief operations, the agencies have been unable to use the ideas-oriented advice from experts and have instead used product-oriented solutions promoted by the 'industry' and other pressure groups. This occurs particularly where the solutions are immediately valuable for publicity (disaster housing for example has high pictorial value) and such solutions have been adopted without research into their applicability to or effect on the populations involved.

The role of designers in this process is ambivalent, reflecting the real conflicts in the profession: on one hand they may be serving as experts analysing situations, producing idea-oriented solutions, and on the other they may be 'selling' a particular product or scheme which is less valuable in the context of disaster relief.

CASE STUDY: DISASTER HOUSING

The particular case I would like to study is that of disaster housing, not only because it has received large quantities of attention and money (estimated at more than $5 million in Managua alone), but also because it represents an 'obvious' requirement in relief operations, which after examination turns out to be not so obvious.

The design of low cost housing is a perennial problem for students at colleges of art and of architecture. In most cases there is a specific reference to disaster housing in poor countries. In 1972 the London Technical Group and the Architectural Association held a meeting on disaster housing and in preparing the meeting some two hundred students' design projects were discovered. From the results of such projects, considerable ingenuity and diversity are apparent, covering all forms (from cubes to domes) and materials (paper, plastics, concrete, steel). The linking feature in these designs is dependence upon a manufactured material and novel constructional techniques. Very few of these designs were built; less were evaluated under field conditions in this country and none was ever used under the full conditions for which it was intended - in a disaster. Thus over the years efforts have been channelled into innovation and diversification rather than into development based on trials, and no attempt has been made to produce a realistic specification based on goals of perform-ance and experience.

There is however a sustained pressure for provision of disaster housing (particularly after earthquakes) both from the public who, seeing reports that homes have been lost, expect relief agencies to provide new ones; and from manufacturers concerned in parts of the building industry like prefabricated shelters and systems building, who feel that their products have a role to play.

The relief agencies have responded massively to this pressure both by supplying commercially available prefabricated buildings and by promoting design programmes themselves. In Lice about 1,000 wooden prefabricated buildings came from Switzerland,

Finland, France and Yugoslavia, but there is very little information available about costs or numbers accommodated. Estimates for Managua vary; Davis (1973) gives about 15,000 prefabricated units supplied from various sources. Of the designs provided by relief agencies, the Oxfam polyurethane is one of the best known; this appeared originally as a dome and latterly, at Lice, as a flat-sided hexagon (in which form some 460 examples were produced).

Despite the very large investments involved, both in money and effort, there is little information about the performance of disaster housing. Davis (1975) found that of forty-six studies covering twelve disasters, only fourteen contained any data at all on housing. But if information is small in quantity, the quality is sufficient for some major conclusions to emerge. Krimgold (1974), in a report on the disaster housing deployed after the Gediz earthquake of 1970, notes that imported prefabricated houses were not well accepted by the local population who found them generally unsatisfactory compared with their original houses. He also comments on the high cost of imports compared to the products of local builders and that a considerable number of locally produced houses were available before the first prefabs. The pattern of disaster housing is also questioned by Davis (1973) who found that in Managua local rebuilding was highly effective and most of the population were evacuated or moved to distant relatives unitl rebuilt houses were available. Cavanagh (1976) in an analysis of disaster housing at Lice, states that local people found all imports unacceptable, particularly the polyurethane foam houses; again he comments on the slowness of imported-house building - some 2,000 local houses were built in the time it took to produce 260 polyurethane foam units. Davis (1976) in discussing emergency shelter, contrasts the generally excellent performance of tents, which are available quickly (usually within a few days) and which are well accepted by local people as a short term solution, and the generally poor performance of disaster housing based on imported prefabs etc, which are expensive, arrive late and are generally culturally unacceptable.

Local housing fulfils the social, physiological and psychological needs of the local people. It is also appropriate to their economy; they are involved in it and can maintain it as required. Immediate shelter, tents in general, provides for physio-logical needs and, in the short term, for the psychological need for security and gathering-together. Intermediate housing, prefabs etc, also provide for physiological needs and, to an extent, for the social needs - to be a family, for example. But neither of these two involve the local people in their design, nor can they easily be locally maintained; their cost will be out of all proportion to the local economic value of housing. There seems little point in putting in the effort and expenditure required for intermediate housing, which is far more expensive than shelter, for no extra advantage - better to put everything into re-housing so that people move straight from shelters into their own rebuilt houses.

The only possible conclusion is that disaster housing is not an unqualified success and that problems have occurred for similar reasons over a considerable time span, at least the five years covered by the cited reports. Now it is often argued that it is better to do something, even if not ideal, than to do nothing whatsoever but I feel that this contains more emotional than logical force, and certainly leads to an unfortunate tendency to do the first something that comes to mind rather than to think carefully

of alternatives. What, for example, if all the money spent had been used to promote
local building; or if materials had been supplied to local builders; or if sites had been
mechanically cleared for them? As it is, disaster housing schemes are characterised
by a lack of careful on-the-spot study and it is perhaps therefore inevitable that
schemes should be unsuccessful in the light of the common misunderstanding of what a
disaster is and of what a house is. The first misconception is that disaster inevitably
leaves people totally dependent upon outside help; an idea which is ill-supported by
studies such as those summarised in Quarantelli and Dynes (1973) who comment on
the high capacity for self-help which exists after disaster. As far as housing itself
is concerned, it is by now a well-worn truism that a house is more than four walls
and a roof - but rather a part of the social mechanism, reflecting a peoples' culture
and pattern of life as well as their need for shelter. Despite this, in an emergency
(with its compressed time scale and a general lack of information about the people
concerned) we switch back to the crudest sort of concept of a house as shelter on the
assumption, presumably, that people will accept anything if they are desperate.

Early this year (1976) a seminar was held by the Disaster Emergency Committee (a
joint fund-raising consortium of British relief agencies) and the Disaster Unit of the
British Ministry of Overseas Development to examine the whole question of disaster
housing. Two papers were given on the analysis of disaster housing - Davis (1976)
(op cit) reporting on experience gained over the last three years and Murlis, Bowden,
Rivers and Holt (1976) which sought to describe physical and social factors in emergency
housing. Interestingly, these two papers came to the same conclusion about the
problem - namely that disaster housing is both unnecessary and undesirable; that
emergency shelter, tents for example, should be provided and that efforts and funds
should be deployed in assisting and encouraging rebuilding.

ASSESSMENT AND EVALUATION

My principal recommendation is that a thoroughly methodical approach to information
collection should be adopted. The diagram shows a classic feedback model for
Assessment and Evaluation in Disaster Relief.

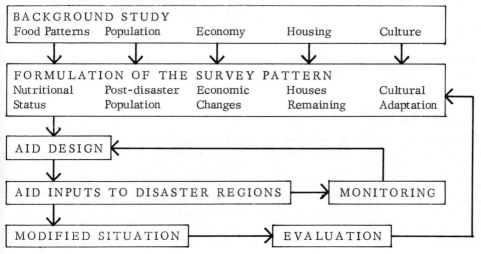

The Background Study is a preliminary exercise used to determine conditions in the region before the disaster and covers such questions as numbers, distribution and groups (eg sedentary or nomadic) of population, their food habits, housing types and culture as well as the kind of local economy involved (eg subsistance or market) and features of local administration. This will provide a valuable first estimate of sequels (for example if an earthquake is involved, information that people are nomadic and living in tents would lead to an expectation that few would have been seriously injured and most people would have packed up and moved out, in contrast to a sedentary population living in masonry-based buildings) and will also clearly indicate areas in which further information is needed. Production of this kind of initial report need not take long. Using sources immediately available, London Technical Group were able to produce a report on Lice within ten days of the 1975 earthquake which proved a valuable, if controversial, tool in aid design.

The next step, the Survey, is carried out to quantify the human effects of the disaster and, again, the time necessary for such a survey need not be excessive except, of course, that information quality increases with time. Rapid survey methods based on a statistical approach were used initially by the Centre for Disease Control of the American Public Health Service. (See for example Summers and Moseley (1972) for an account of an initial assessment of the human situation in East Bengal following the November 1970 cyclone, carried out by four two-man teams in five days.) More recently the London Technical Group has developed these techniques to give a broader assessment of conditions by placing nutritional and medical findings in a social and economic context (eg Seaman, Holt and Rivers (1974) on Haraghe province of Ethiopia). From survey information, it is then possible to design a relief programme. It is important that design should be carried out in this manner even if some delay is entailed since wrong aid is often worse than no aid. (It blocks local reception systems, consumes funds in competition with 'correct' aid and may have ill effects upon the local economy by generation of dependence on black markets.) In the model shown, Aid Imports to the disaster region lead to a Modification of the situation and two feedback loops are shown. The first loop, Monitoring, should be carried out to ensure that imports are as intended but it is the second loop, the Evaluation of the modified situation, which is crucial to progress in relief aid design. Evaluation is carried out through a similar process as that used in a preliminary survey and enables the aid donor to see the effects of inputs - it is this process that highlighted the failure of disaster housing described above. But a recent evaluation carried out in Guatemala, Wemys & Holt (1976), shows that the message has not percolated through to agencies yet.

THE DISASTER SITUATION

Information collected by the process outlined above leads to an improvement in knowledge about human ramifications of disasters and has brought about some tentative results, which must be taken as guidelines rather than general truths. A distinction can be made between abrupt events, such as an earthquake or a cyclone, and the gradual effects of drought or extreme poverty seen, for example, in famine. To an extent this is an artificial division, since over a period of time the abrupt event may lead to problems usually seen in gradual disasters, but it may be helpful in this discussion to differentiate between conditions after the immediate effects of sudden events and those to be found when for example, a famine is belatedly discovered (as is invariably the case).

Thus, in an abrupt disaster subsequent mortality will usually be below normal, frail groups having suffered heavily in the initial catastrophe (see Summers and Mosely, op cit), whereas in famine one might expect a slightly higher mortality which will be age and sex specific depending upon patterns of food distribution. Strong evidence exists that morale is high after abrupt disaster (see Quarantelli and Dynes op cit) and although there is anecdotal evidence of low morale amongst famine victims, this is by no means universally accepted. Changes in family structure can have important implications for aid requirements (for example, lack of adult men will slow reconstruction) and also create social tensions.

In an abrupt disaster changes will be largely a function of when the catastrophe occurred. If an earthquake occurred in the day time with men working in the fields, women left in the villages would be the main victims. Where there is a situation of increasing difficulty, such as in the period leading up to an observed famine, there is a tendency for families to break up as men move away in search of work or new land. (Holt (1975) on the inhabitants of relief shelters in Wollo in 1973 described how women and children formed a disproportionate majority of those living in shelters, the men having gone to neighbouring towns seeking work.)

In the highly technologically developed countries of the world, a disaster is seen as a time of great physical suffering and this view is reflected in the huge proportion of aid devoted to medical relief. But is this a true picture? Lechat (1973) discusses earthquakes from an epidemiologist's viewpoint and declares that apart from minor injuries, medical problems will be as before the catastrophe - certainly there will not be a decline in general health sufficient by itself to justify expenditure on medical relief. Medical teams do always find work to do, but it is usually the treatment of endemic diseases and minor ailments: such work is dangerous as it creates expectancies that the service will continue after the relief agencies have moved on, and represents an unequitable distribution of services throughout a country. The one proviso in this is that public health measures can be taken to control sufficiently the spread of the 'diseases of chaos' - water borne infections such as typhoid. In famine, it is mainly the endemic diseases which are found, perhaps in some cases slightly increased by low nutrition.

Physical changes in famine are not generally disruptive as, for example, the collapse of buildings and destruction of water supplies in an earthquake, but there is often abandonment (as in Ethiopia, where farmers left their lands and villages) and in these cases there may be a need for shelter more urgent than that found after earthquake.

This overall picture of disasters does not conform to the view generally held in rich donor countries: it is rather one of people with very specific problems, but with a strong capacity for finding the solutions themselves. But one further important view of disaster is that of the national government. The national government must take a much broader view than donors of aid inputs; large sums of money spent on emergency aid may be seen as overriding these priorities. For example, if a government is trying gradually to improve rural medical services, an input to a region struck by

catastrophe, of high technology medical facilities costing several times the government's
annual health budget, is bound to cause resentment in other regions and the government
will be resentful in thinking what it could have done itself, given that cost in money.
Neither are agencies saving governments from spending their own money: the disaster
may have but a small impact upon the overall economy, regardless of its cost in life,
and the government of a poor country cannot risk its precarious solvency by large
expenditure on a single region.

In the disaster situation, people may move temporarily by going to stay with relations,
as in Managua, Bangladesh or now, Guatemala: or they may move permanently, as
nomads would do. Structures may be repaired, as at Lice, or a temporary shelter
may be erected for use whilst rebuilding takes place in the traditional manner. In
many parts of the world where catastrophic events are common, there are traditional
standbys - such as the woven mat 'tents' made by Bengali villagers as a first shelter
after a cyclone, or the foods traditionally used in times of shortage of other more
appealing food (eg those listed by Seaman et al (op cit) for Upper Volta). It is unfortunately all too rare for people to rebuild in an improved manner; that is, to build
incorporating experience into improved structures: Davis (1976) is encouraging the
use in Guatemala of a diagonal strut to stabilise open-frames, a simple but
important innovation. A final response is to do nothing, resulting largely from the
frustration which arises when people are denied access to the resources they need to
help themselves whilst strangers fumble.

DESIGN STRATEGIES

The foregoing is intended as a review of the factors which must be taken into consideration by designers approaching disaster relief. It should be obvious that knowledge
about the recipients is essential to successful design: in fact, without such knowledge
there is no point at all in embarking upon a project. Furthermore, although agencies
are in a sense the customer, it should be to the recipient that the designers devote
their loyalty. Various design strategies emerge and it is now possible to review the
options.

A system may be entirely imported, like the foam domes, making no contribution to
the local economy or labour market. Such solutions are relatively expensive and
suffer from poor acceptability.

A second option is to use local materials with imported expertise, and a good example
of this is the shelter design produced by students at Carnegie Mellon University (with
others) which is really an improvement on a local design, increasing strength and
resistance to environmental conditions. By the use of local materials and labour
there results a shelter which is understood by local people and which they can adapt
and modify as required.

Another alternative is to use local expertise with imported materials, as in the supply
of polythene sheet to Bengal, which was used in various ways by local builders. Again
this puts the controls in the hands of the recipients. The danger, however, is
development of a market for imported materials and subsequent economic dependence,
although this effect has not been measured.

Given the well-documented local capacity for self-help, it is surprising that assistance in local effort as a fourth option has suffered relative neglect, particularly since it offers a vast scope for relief agencies. Amongst the many things that can be done are the following:

> Site clearance and preparation.
>
> Provision of transport facilities for moving materials.
>
> Provision of cash payments for labour.
>
> Loan schemes for purchase of materials: (given that an abnormally large amount of material may be needed all at once).
>
> Loan of hand tools.

In fact anything which facilitates or encourages rebuilding in the specific context (right down to paying a local singer to ease the burden of work) forms part of this strategy. An example in practice was the digging of trenches in Turkey by bulldozer which, roofed over by local people, formed useful emergency shelter (Ambraseys 1968).

There may be occasions when local efforts are delayed by shortages of materials or by the time needed to perform certain operations (jointing timbers for example) and minimal inputs of shortages, carefully chosen, might speed up the process:

> Analogue materials, that is materials having the same properties as local materials but readily available elsewhere, may be imported to be used as substitutes. (Some use iron as an analogue of wood.)
>
> Fittings for doors or windows could be supplied under an exchange scheme with overseas suppliers, or purchased in regional centres.
>
> Substituting speedier methods such as nailed joints for wooden-pegged joints.
>
> Prepared foundations, as in the site and services schemes of Cuny (1971).

There is little practical experience of this strategy, but it seems a fruitful one for designers.

The sixth option is one of the most difficult to accept: there are occasions in which local effort is entirely self-sufficient and no outside intervention is required. The only thing to be done is to learn from such occasions, for they represent an ideal case of disaster relief.

The last option is education. The education programme in Guatemala, aimed at improving building stability (already mentioned), is an example. Other possibilities spring to mind where education is aimed not at radical change, but at specific marginal improvements, such as more economic use of materials, faster construction techniques or safer siting.

DESIGN PRINCIPLES

In the study of disaster relief are found certain recurrent features of successful operations and these suggest that there are principles having at least some degree of universality, which can be a practical guide to designers. I have formulated these principles in the following list, which is intended as a starting point rather than a full and comprehensive list. The elements listed are not options; ideally they should all be followed and certainly they should all be considered.

> Field Experience. Problems can only be identified from experience of conditions after disaster: so many complex and interrelating factors are present that attempts to anticipate problems can lead to misidentification and a subsequent distortion of priority areas for further investigation.

> Full evaluation. Problems must be fully evaluated to establish the need for outside help and, if such a need should exist, to determine the precise nature of the problem and its human context.

> Use of survey data. There are ways of quantifying human need and designers should make use of these methods in determining the scale of the problem and in forming a data base to which reference can be made during design.

> Multi-disciplinary approach. Some of the more glaringly inappropriate features of disaster housing might have been eliminated at an early stage had design not been solely in the hands of designers, since the social ramifications of housing are a branch of sociology. Because of the many factors involved it seems essential to involve specialists in different subjects in the design process at the earliest possible stage, and not simply to refer designs to a committee for endorsement. It is a point of debate whether designers are themselves multi-disciplinary, but it is my contention that it is better to involve a set of well-read specialists than to rely on a group of generalists specialising in design.

> Minimise inputs. Harness local capacity, materials and skills. The local capacity for rebuilding has been mentioned above. Large scale imports of materials, labour and expertise are not only unsatisfactory in themselves, they also have considerable ill-effects upon the local economy, self-esteem and attitudes towards foreign assistance. Understanding local efforts and providing only the things which are genuinely lacking will minimise the ill-effects initially and in the long term will help to build the reputation of foreign aid.

> Restore the familiar. Studies of psychology in disaster show

that one outstanding human need exists: the need for restoration of the familiar patterns of life and surroundings (see Murlis et al). The period following a disaster is not the time to encourage a people to change dietary patterns or to live in strangely shaped houses. In fact, many of the familiar aspects will be adhered to more tightly after the disaster - for example religious ritual might assume a more important role as a link with the time before the disaster. The designers' aim should be to assist the people concerned to restore their lives to the familiar pattern.

Evaluate results of input. It is only by learning from experience that design can be improved, so that no project can be considered completed until the process of evaluation has been carried out.

THE DESIGNER'S ROLE

The role of the designer in disaster relief, therefore, is to use his/her training, experience and creative imagination to guide a project through each stage, from initial investigation to evaluation, without compromising the interests of the recipient.

To summarise the process of design: after a full evaluation of available information, problem areas can be identified and the designer's role at this stage will be to ensure that a need exists for a design-solution, which in the light of the foregoing, may not be certain. After a full exploration of alternatives, involving the widest possible spectrum of disciplines, a solution can be synthesised and deployed in the knowledge that modifications will be needed as information on performance emerges. The full process of evaluation and modification may take a considerable length of time and the designer must be prepared to accept at the outset that involvement over many years may be necessary.

But in future, designers must also be careful to consider whether to be involved in specific disaster relief projects at all and, having convinced themselves that need exists, must base solutions upon the fullest possible understanding of the local people, their life styles and customs. The aim should be to restore life as it existed before the disaster and to ensure that the future of the community remains to be decided by the local people themselves.

In many cases, nothing will be required. Often some small well-chosen input can contribute to the speed and success of 'rebuilding'. (Elaborate or technologically dependent design should be avoided.) The designer thus contributes most significantly by quietly learning about local conditions and exercising his role as unobtrusively as possible.

A RANGE OF EASY CHAIRS FOR THE ADULT DISABLED AND ELDERLY FRAIL

Russell Manoy

Easy chairs for the disabled and elderly have been available for a considerable time, but it is only in recent years that any constructive attention has been focussed on their design. Much of the earlier development came from within the hospitals and was based on the subjective judgement of staff with no skill or training in depicting variety of posture. Evaluation of the chairs available was similarly subjective. The one exception (Bramwell Jones, 1969) was based on a questionnaire circulated to a limited number of experts, and in many situations their recommendations were either impracticable or not economically feasible.

Even now there is a serious lack of ergonomic data. One of the few sources of information (Roberts 1960) is based on static anthropometric data in the form of dimensions such as buttock to knee, elbow height, etc. Although helpful to designers this does not go far enough.

And so the aim of our study has been to investigate thoroughly the requirements for a range of easy chairs for the disabled adult and elderly frail. The prime factors considered were the size characteristics and the extent of loss of function. As the data must be displayed clearly and unambiguously for the use of designers in industry, it is presented in two forms: tabulated data on all critical body dimensions and a series of sectional curves in the sagittal plane. From these it is possible to derive either graphic or numerical data for a given percentile (with mean and standard deviations) of a given group of disabilities.

The first part of the project was a series of sessions at six hospitals in the South of England based on experiments at Abingdon Hospital under the guidance of Dr Philip Nichols, Director of Mary Margaret Lodge, Oxford, and advisor to the Department of Health and Social Security on physical medicine. One hundred and fifty-four subjects were selected to represent various groups classified by sex, age, weight, height and disability. A plaster cast was made for each subject by means of an adjustable mould. The rig consisted of a modified hospital bed with a bag mattress filled with polystyrene beads. The beads could be locked in a given position by sucking the air from the mattress with a vacuum pump. The rig was set to an angle of 104° between seat to back. With the subject in position the bag was gently manoeuvred around him or her to record the body shape, with special attention to the lumbar area, the elbows, head and other points of contact such as the under-knee. The subject was then helped out and a plaster cast built up on the mattress mould with conventional plaster of paris bandages a process that took from 15 to 25 minutes and was repeated 154 times.

The next stage of the project was to actually measure the plaster casts. A rig was designed to obtain the data using a simplified version of the copy lathe technique. The centre line of each cast was marked (most satisfactorily done by eye in the event)

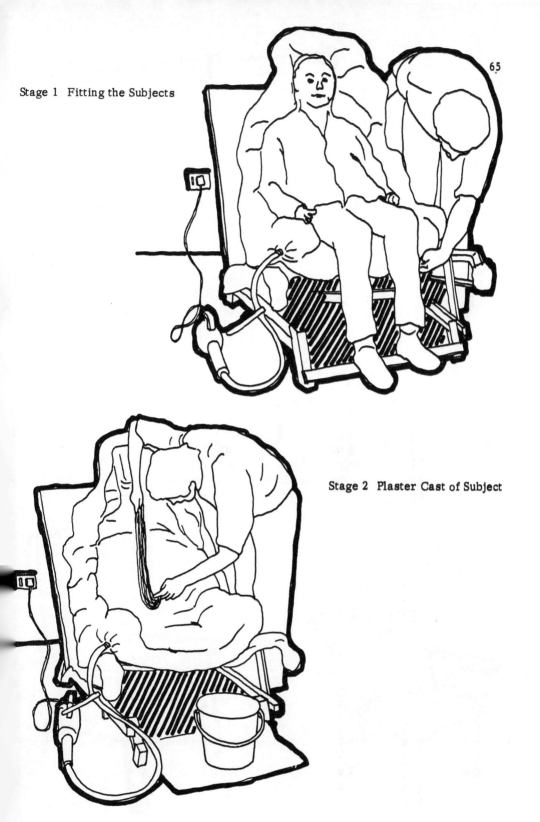

Stage 1   Fitting the Subjects

Stage 2   Plaster Cast of Subject

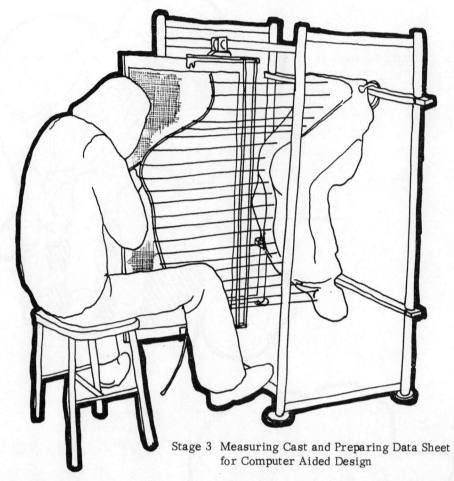

Stage 3 Measuring Cast and Preparing Data Sheet
for Computer Aided Design

Fully Adjustable Test Rig
for User Trials

Prototype of Large Chair III

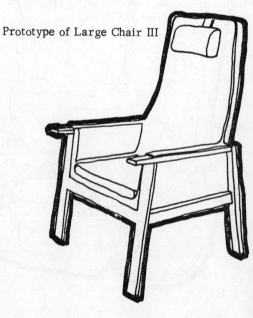

through the centre of the head, down the spine to the base of the back ending under the knee. This was one of the critical datum lines for the computer, the other being the angle between back and seat. The cast was then positioned on the measuring rig and the seven sagittal curves plotted at 25mm intervals, the distances of the sections either side of the centre varying according to the individual. The measurements were transferred on to full size data sheets, each colour-coded for the distance right or left of the centre.

The sheets were then handed to the Computer Aided Design Centre at the Royal College of Art where the data was digitised on to paper tape. Several programmes were then run to try and establish sub-groups among the 154 subjects. The body shapes were collated in three basic ways: by numerical value (rather meaningless in this case), by the use of scatter diagrams, and by the similarity of body curves. The last grouping to be tried based on the convexity and concavity of each individual cast proved the most successful. Four logical chair groups emerged: convex and short, convex and tall, normal, or concave. A conventional scaling procedure was used to ascertain the percentile ranges and produce full size sagittal sections at the 95th, mean and 5th percentile for all four chairs.

At the completion of the analysis it was vital to check the project by carrying out a short series of user trials. Six backs and four seats were constructed based on the percentile values. Forty-eight subjects were selected from the sex, age, height, weight and disability groupings previously discussed. Absolutely no attempt was made to style the chair structure in order to minimise the subjective visual response. A fairly extensive questionnaire related to heights, widths, lengths, degree of curvature and angle etc, was put to the subjects while in the chairs. Despite insufficient time there was a positive response to the shapes. Based on the findings of these user trials, final prototypes are now under construction.

Until the mid sixties there was a general reluctance to discuss the ramifications of disablement, such as easy chairs. This was due in part to the philosophy of hiding the disabled away rather than tackling the task of rehabilitation. Professionals such as designers have helped to remedy this situation and there has been a much needed change in the overall approach to the welfare of the disabled and elderly. Unfortunately much of the finance and many of the workers in this field are channelled toward the more emotive disabilities and the types of equipment they require. I am sure that these products and those working on them require all the assistance they receive, but is it right to give the vast majority of finance and resources towards as little as 5% of the disabled population while 95% remains under-equipped? Such items as the range of easy chairs I have discussed are not particularly profound in their appeal or contribution to society. However, charitable organisations such as my sponsoring body - The National Fund for Research into Crippling Diseases - should be congratulated for supporting such a wide-based research project. Let us hope that others will follow this example.

LOW HANDICAP TECHNOLOGY:
THE REDUCTION OF NEED BY
DESIGN
John Mitchell

My title refers to the reduction of need by design and I will begin by explaining what I mean by need, and how design can affect need. I consider that need derives from responsibility. Each of us has a certain number of responsibilities which are of such importance that serious consequences result from failing to carry them out. We have responsibilities to ourselves, and on occasion to other people.

Our most basic responsibility is to ourselves, in that we should maintain our physical well-being. We must keep ourselves nourished, clean, warm and acceptably dressed and in close contact with our surroundings. We take a pride in accepting this responsibility in our early lives and experience considerable suffering at any failures of performance through lack of forethought, incapacity or maybe inebriation. These responsibilities are shared with all other humans in society and we have a recurring need to fulfil them regularly and adequately.

Arising from these daily responsibilities we must make provision for obtaining necessary materials. This involves us in the processes of education, training and employment.

Often responsibilities are traded and one member of a household will accept family responsibility for earning an income whilst another accepts responsibility for running the household. As before, serious consequences arise if these responsibilities cannot be met, and the well-being of a family is likely to suffer as a result. The care services of the country have been established to meet these needs, based on such unavoidable responsibilities.

If a responsibility cannot be met by an individual then a need remains unsatisfied and requires intervention to avert the consequences. I would like to turn to the factors which lead to need being unsatisfied - to do this I must explain the term handicap. Handicap is the unsuccessful interaction between users and their environments. To illustrate this, I would like to adapt Bauer's Formula:

$$HANDICAP = \frac{ENVIRONMENTAL\ DEMANDS}{POPULATION\ ABILITIES}$$

In order to reduce the left hand side of the equation (the amount of handicap within a population) we can:

Either improve the ability of the population,

Or reduce the demands of the environment.

68

Traditionally, we have taken an individualistic approach to this problem and have assumed that when a person is unable to fulfil a responsibility, the fault for this should be laid at his door. We therefore encourage him or berate him, we rehabilitate him or we provide him with a series of one-off special solutions to his difficulties, perhaps a toilet raise or a stocking putter-onner. I am dubious of the wisdom of continuing to commit ourselves to this approach in the future. It would seem to me that if a great number of people in a population are unable to meet their needs without extensive special provisions then there is something radically wrong with their environments.

If we reduce the need for users to be adaptable by providing environments which are compatible with the ability of all our population, we immediately remove the barrier between responsibility and its fulfilment for a large number of those who are handicapped at present, and by our design we reduce the amount of unmet need.

In the recent past, environments have been designed for a population of strangely adaptable people. Designers may have been asked to design equipment for activities with which they were unfamiliar. Many pieces of equipment have been introduced without the benefit of well-tested forerunners on which to base the designs. It is possible also that our domestic environments were so well staffed by servants (who had the advantage of not only being cheap and adaptable but also replaceable) that we had no need to reduce environmental demands.

But the number of handicapped and impaired people in Great Britain is roughly 5,000,000. This gives a ratio of about one handicapped person in every ten of the population. The likelihood of an average five person family including a handicapped or impaired person is approaching fifty per cent. So the reduction of handicap affects one in every two families.

Any increase in the level of public spending however would seem most unlikely. We are therefore compelled to reconsider our approach to making provision for handicap. If we provide environments which demand considerable adaptability from the users, then we must be prepared to pay an ever increasing cost for special services and equipment to avoid the consequences. Since we cannot meet extra costs we must provide environments which are compatible with the abilities of the whole population or ignore the unmet need.

The starting point for introducing low handicap technology should be in the home. This requires a considerable amount of redesign to improve the equipment which is used in the bathroom, bedroom and kitchen. Before any equipment, system or environment can be used without restraint by all members of the population it is essential that:

> Access should be unobstructed.

> No awkward or extreme postures should be demanded of the users.

> Adequate postural support should be available, both for occasional and for long term static postures.

Nobody would deny that a small step at a threshold will eliminate a small number of

elderly and impaired people from entry. But while the incorporation of a hurdle
would eliminate most of us, we hardly notice the existence of small barriers and
are unaware of the handicap which is imposed. In the same way we are well able to
stoop to reach goods stored under a work surface. We can adopt the awkward posture
and maintain it for long enough. But is it of any advantage to accept this posture? Do
we really wish to buy a unit which will become more difficult to use as we become
older? Or should we organise our storage facilities so as to be readily accessible to
us all whether we are fit or lame?

We are also familiar with the need of humans to be in continual motion. Joseph and
others have pointed out that we oscillate rather than stand still and Basmajion has
shown that gentle walking is less demanding than standing in one place. (We all know
that prolonged use of any one position, particularly where static musclework is
involved can make subsequent movement difficult.) These characteristics have been
recognised, but only in limited and surprising situations. In public bars we provide
a rich variety of postural support for standing, sitting or lounging, yet in our kitchens
we make provision for one posture only, that of standing.

However, unless there are clear advantages available for the manufacturers who must
bear the costs and risks of development, it is unlikely that any substantial changes
will occur. If this proposed product differs considerably from the accepted product,
the manufacturer runs the risk of failing to convince the public of the advantages
available. Customer expectations will have to change before a market can be firmly
established. This process may not be easy to carry out using arguments such as
'Buy this and make your old age and decrepitude easier to bear. '

The risk may be high, but on the other hand, the market potential is very great.
Large numbers of customers, government agencies and local authorities for example,
are in no position to turn down equipment which does not require replacement or
costly alteration when a user's adaptability starts to diminish.

But in some areas, the introduction of low handicap technology would be an immensely
costly undertaking. The wholesale adaptation of permanent structures, such as the
London underground, would cost nearly as much as an entirely new system. And so
we may be stuck with some of our high handicap, but cherished, environments.

Fortunately this is not true in the field of domestic equipment where we have the
benefit of a strange process known as obsolescence. This much criticised feature of
design has the great advantage that, no matter how good or bad a particular model
may be, it will be replaced by another within the space of a few years. Accordingly,
it is possible to slip in low handicap equipment at the cost of a little extra research,
design and evaluation work, plus, of course, the cost of changing production techniques

A low handicap environment can allow the population to meet its needs without special
intervention, and since our ability to provide special intervention is low, the time is
now right for learning to build our equipment and environments to suit all who must use
them. In the next paper Janet Hall describes an example of the approach in practice.

AN ERGONOMIC ANALYSIS OF
PERSONAL HYGIENE ACTIVITIES
Janet Hall

Aids are a human and laudable attempt to alter the characteristics of the environment so as to make it amenable to those whose physical compliance is low. But would it not be better to produce environments which can be used by all members of the population without (or with the very minimum of) aids?

There are plenty of reasons for discontinuing the practice of providing specialised aids:

> Aids are expensive to purchase and few have been tested or evaluated.

> Considerable amounts of staff time are required to assess patients and to train them in the use of their aids.

> Many aids, though taken home by the patient, are not used.

> Many people reject aids even though they are at risk or barely able to manage without them.

The environment which we chose to use as an example is the bathroom. Twenty-seven subjects were questioned as to the equipment and posture they used while carrying out different hygiene activities. Analysis of the results showed that certain requirements were basic to all subjects irrespective of their age or physical condition: postural support, access, water supply and drainage.

However, there were distinct differences in the amount of support required by a young man or woman who can balance on one foot while washing the other, and by a disabled subject who requires to be seated and to have maximal contact with his environment before carrying out the same activity. Also, difficulties of access present few problems to agile subjects but are of critical importance to the elderly or the disabled.

All standard bathrooms can be criticised for the scarcity and the inadequate nature of supporting surfaces and for the difficulties of access to the bathtub and basin. As these features of conventional equipment cannot be said to satisfy the basic human requirements of the situation, we must now establish if they can be replaced with alternatives. Is it possible to provide adequate postural support, water supply and drainage with unimpeded access ... and does such equipment impose a low level of handicap on its users and make the use of aids unnecessary?

In fact there is no difficulty in producing such a facility, based on the use of moveable showers for water supply and peripheral shelves for postural support. Indeed, such facilities can provide a wider range of postural support than is available with conventional bathroom equipment and at the same time require a much reduced floor area due to the integration of separate pieces of equipment.

The original unit was exposed to dry trials using a sample of nine barely ambulant subjects. The results of first trials led to further research to determine the viability of our ergonomic hypothesis. The aim was to determine whether the unit could be made satisfactory for all users, including manufacturer, purchaser, installer, maintainer, as well as the conventionally termed user.

To achieve this, more comprehensive ergonomic trials were executed using thirty able bodied and disabled subjects, representing a greater range of physical capacity and age. The results of these trials, despite the modification, confirmed the validity of the ergonomic principals. Investigations into appropriate materials, plumbing, environmental control, construction and installation methods etc were made. Also the effects of existing architecture were studied and incorporated into the dimensions and layout of the unit.

A third trial was conducted at Ingo Simon House, Mount Vernon Hospital with an almost fully operational unit (WC use was excluded). Eleven subjects, again representing a range of physical ability and age, conducted activities in wet conditions. The use of the unit was carefully studied and subjective responses to the appearance of the unit were recorded. The results confirmed the unit's ergonomic superiority over the conventional bathroom, particularly for disabled or elderly persons, both ambulant and wheelchair bound. The unit's appearance was considered very acceptable both by able bodied and disabled alike and preferable to the multiplicity of separate aids normally associated with bathroom use by the disabled.

Three full studies were made. One was to compile a rough guide on local authority expenditure on installing or modifying bathrooms for both able bodied and disabled persons. The second was to discover the range of prices of equipment being used for this work. The third and largest (three hundred questionnaires) was a market survey to determine those areas where the advantages found in the unit would be of definite value. This survey, although very diverse, was ultimately based on the degree of dissatisfaction the respondents had with their present equipment (or lack of it) and a correlation of their requirements with the advantages the unit offers.

These surveys defined clear prospective markets, including houses designated for improvement by local authorities, houses of disabled persons requiring bathroom modification, hospitals, hostels and old peoples homes, colleges, computer complexes, holiday homes, caravans and boats, as well as those who are pregnant or elderly and those who require second bathrooms. Given these market areas, a unit is estimated to cost £300.

This three year period of work demonstrates that redesign of the bathroom environment is desirable for ergonomic and social reasons and that such redesign is not only possible but also offers material advantages: the reduction of space used by the unit and the ancillary equipment, and the minimal labour content needed for installation and operation. Most important, the need for aids in the new design has been virtually eliminated so that the great majority of disabled and elderly people can be accommodated in an environment equally suited to the able bodied public.

THE ROLE OF THE ARTIST IN A HOSPITAL ENVIRONMENT
John Smalley

All activities and forms that a society produces are in some measure a reflection of the meaning that it attaches to life. Specialisation, a product of our machine orientated society, has fostered a tendency towards fragmentation and compartment-alisation. We feel it necessary to go beyond perceptual distinctions - we divide our community into groups (pensioners, the ill, the mentally deficient). We feel it necessary to locate these groups and to separate them from each other and from the more integrated areas of our society, Our institutions are formed to contain these divisions, and reflect our attitude to these groups. Institutions tend to accentuate isolation, since they are often only structured to one specific area of activity: 'a piazza for everything and everything in its piazza' (Marshall McLuhan). The placing of many of our so-called problem groups into such limiting structures is one example of how we differ from certain other societies. We prevent interaction between the young and the aged, the ill and the healthy, and by separation we diminish the areas of experience possible to us as human beings. In contrast the medieval age produced a perspective on life that was directed towards unity. It presented itself as a highly systematised theocentric society, containing its own forms of social defects, yet it seems to have related to many of the basic needs that have been neglected by the modern state - a frame of orientation and devotion, a truly individual sense of identity, a need for rootedness and a need to relate to and transcend the state of passivity. We have sufficient grounds for questioning the structuring of our society in the light of these needs and we may well find that single purpose institutions are no longer desirable in their present form.

Similarly the questioning of our concepts of health may result in a change in the functioning of the hospital and the nature of the hospital environment. The 'Huang Ti Nei Ching', an ancient Chinese treatise on medicine, says:

> 'The inferior physician begins to help when the disease has
> already developed, he helps when destruction has already set
> in. And since his help comes when the disease has already
> developed, it is said of him that he is ignorant.'

Despite the brilliant results in the curing of endemic diseases by modern medicine, our attitude to health seems to have been less effectual. The system that we have created has been almost totally concerned with the combating of illness rather than its prevention. (There is a Chinese practice whereby doctors are only paid when the client is enjoying perfect health.) With the acceptance by many medical practitioners of the psychosomatic origin of certain forms of illness, more is being attempted in terms of treating the patient in relation to his social and psychological background. The dictum of Socrates, that you should not treat body without soul, may still be considered as an effective principle for modern medicine.

The physical environment is a major factor that can affect the patient's mental state
and consequently can aid or retard his recovery to health. While 19th century
reformers, like Chadwick, rightly stressed the importance of hygienic conditions
in preventing the possibility of infection, the 20th century has made the term 'hygiene'
signify 'sterility' and 'bland clinical surroundings'. In India the western style hospitals
are regarded as cold inhuman places and many people prefer to be treated in the
Ayurvedic hospitals, despite the fact that they are not as well equipped. Even though
the average length of stay in a hospital in England is now approximately only ten days,
it is a period of intense pressure for most people. It is important therefore that the
images of life can be experienced within this environment in all their variety. In fact
the suppression of these images may itself be the cause of mental illness, the surroundings having failed to supply sufficient stimulus for the individual to realise
aspects of his unconscious. The need for art in a hospital environment, not as a
token gesture to cultural refinement, but as a dynamic aspect of the environment, is
evident.

The extent to which this need can be fulfilled is dependent on the willingness of the
artist to work in a community context and on the community offering both encourage-
ment and employment to him. The first condition is inextricably linked to the artist's
view of himself and his role in our society.

The inclination of many contemporary artists to search for meaning at the peripheries
of human existence, avoiding wherever possible traditionally accepted forms of
language and embracing wherever possible paradox, dichotomous elements and a huge
reservoir of ingenious devices for the mystification of the uninitiated, does not provide
the best of references for their involvement in community art projects. In contrast the
art of primitive societies is essentially communal and functional, woven into the total
fabric of life to be experienced by all and understood on various levels. The fostering
of the artist's individuality is still possible within such a framework and his personalised
vision need not be compromised by a consideration of collective areas of response.
Questions regarding the social obligation of the artist are far too complex to be
discussed fully here, and often we need persons with the required ability to perform
the task as much as the legislation and planning necessary to utilise their services.
We can however attempt to create a climate within which the talent available can be
used in more purposeful ways. We could attempt to create an equilibrium between
analysis and synthesis, between the search for forms and their application, like theory
and practice, like breathing in and breathing out. And we can attempt to use the
resources available to us, our artists, our colleges and museums to the greater
benefit of the whole of our society. The commissioning of artists for isolated projects
and the purchasing of their work has not provided serious alternatives to the gallery
situation which has monopolised the attention of artists and greatly influenced the form
of their art.

More successful alternatives have been provided from larger federal projects for
public art. The WPA programme in America and the Mexican wall paintings come
to mind. The formation of national and local arts councils may have furthered the
possibility of development in public art. Financial aid in the form of grants and
commissions, and employment of a more permanent nature could provide incentive
for the creation of public art. Policies and legislation on the issue of financing art

for public buildings exist in some countries. In Sweden one per cent of the money
spent on public buildings is allocated to the purchasing of art for these buildings.
A re-evaluation of the distribution of present funds may also be desirable for there
seems to be a discrepancy between the amounts of money used for research into the
function of hospital furniture and equipment for the benefit of hospital employees
and the amount spent on enriching the environment and increasing facilities for the
benefit of the patients.

A way of affecting the use of art in a hospital environment is to include an artist in
a design group which is responsible for the total environment of the building,
preferably as close to the inception of the building as possible. In Stockholm, a
special working group 'Ag Miljo' was appointed to plan the total environment of the
Huddinge Hospital consisting of hospital employees, representatives from Stockholm's
county council, artists, an architect and an interior designer. They were responsible
for creating and co-ordinating interior decor, colours, surfaces, shapes, lighting,
furniture, textiles, signposting, art and activities mainly of a recreational nature.
This committee formed smaller groups, three of which were involved in the purchasing
of art.

In addition to the environmental design that may be planned for tomorrow's hospitals,
there is the problem of existing hospital environments and their potential improvement.
The work of an artist in this field usually entails providing the patch for the 'eye-sore'
and demands a certain ability to improvise. In many cases the nature of the 'eye-sore'
or 'planning oversight' dictates the form that the camouflage will take.

During 1975 students from the painting school at the Royal College of Art were
involved in a project that typified the problem of gilding lilies of a rather dubious
quality. The Royal Marsden Hospital, Sutton (a hospital concerned solely in the
treatment of cancer), contains a basement corridor approximately 130ft in length.
A donation of £500, collected by an ex-patient and her charity group, was made to
effect a transformation of this area. The corridor connects a lift area to the main
radium treatment unit containing two treatment rooms, a reception area and a series
of external cubicles and small store rooms. Patients are obliged to journey through
the corridor, either being wheeled in chairs or on trolleys, or walking. The corridor,
was originally lit entirely by tungsten lighting and painted a glossy cream. It was a
nightmare mixture of austere rectangular shapes and dazzling reflections. The
students sought opinions from the staff and patients of the hospital as to the type of
imagery they would like to see in their environment. Eventually three major concepts
were agreed upon:

> The images used could be read sequentially and the content
> could be thematic and relate to the activity of journeying
> through the corridor.

> The images should not accentuate the rectangular format and
> directional element of the architecture.

> The images should be in the form of a series of 'stations'
> appearing at intervals along the corridor rather than a
> continuous image stretching its full length.

The idea was to transform the corridor into an avenue of tree designs inspired by plant life. Triangles on the walls and ovals on the ceiling were used to provide basic geometric shapes within which to work. Changes of colour and form relating to seasonal elements, arithmetical progressions and symbols referring to 'evolutionary cycles' were incorporated. The triangular wall shapes were placed alternately on the walls of the corridor (never opposite each other). As one journeys through the corridor, the images are viewed in a rhythmic motion cutting across the lineal direction of the corridor.

The benefits achieved by encouraging students as well as established artists to work in this field are numerous. The students gain an awareness of the use of art in a social context; an experience of environmental design, of dealing with actual problems and the effort that is required to complete. Unlike 'theoretical designing', the student is confronted with the reality of transposing his designs and ideas into different scales and spatial orders. The experience and the knowledge acquired by working in an existing hospital environment would prove invaluable in the designing of future hospitals. The hospital may also gain from this invasion of their hierarchy by entertaining a section of society whose aims and perspectives, though not necessarily diametrically opposed, do perhaps differ from the normal day to day concerns of the hospital. Hopefully, the hospital would acquire a more stimulating, interesting and human environment.

In the case of Huddinge Hospital and the Royal Marsden Hospital the involvement of artists was temporary. Although the work may prove to have a long term effect it can be viewed as a gesture of introduction at the meeting of two worlds. A well proven procedure following the sending of emissaries, is the establishing of an embassy. The positioning of an 'artist in residence' in a hospital could provide further opportunities for varied art activities to take place. As well as being involved in working on aspects of the physical environment the artist could perhaps involve the staff and patients in their own environment and co-operate with therapy activities. Art classes, lectures and discussions could be made available and an area could be utilised as a gallery in which artists would be invited to exhibit work. The artist could liaise with tutors and students of colleges and offer projects that could be incorporated within the hospital building. Other activities and events could be organised for the benefit of staff and patients. A greater understanding of the needs of people in hospitals would be gained from a venture of this nature, an understanding which could be used in the planning of future hospitals. Dual or multi-purpose buildings can be envisaged where cinemas, youth centres and sports clubs may be incorporated into buildings that also have sections catering for the ill or the physically or mentally incapacitated (a hospital building could contain a theatre for acting as well as one for extracting).

Obviously there are many aspects of the role of the artist and the nature of art in a hospital environment that could be the subject for discussion. However I wish to outline two attitudes that, more than others, seemed to have affected the presentation of art in hospitals. The first concerns the positioning of art in hospitals. In most cases, if not all, eighty per cent of the art purchased for the buildings is found in the main entrance, the reception area and others directly connected to these. This may benefit the visitors and out-patients and is usually quite prestigious to the hospital but cannot affect the patients' condition. Wards are usually neglected and one can envisage that permanent works of art in these areas could present problems. Yet here often the only alternative to staring for hours at a white ceiling is the pleasure of staring for hours at the chrysanthemums, bed pan and lucozade bottle belonging to the patient opposite, all suitably framed by the inevitable Hockney print.

The vetting of images that may disturb the patient, the rejection of forms that may present analogies with subjects of an unsuitable nature (particularly death) has resulted in the presentation of a type of art that is almost totally devoid of any depth of meaning. Also, misconceptions about the nature and psychology of colour abound.

One would have to search hard within hospital buildings to find reproductions of work by Bacon, Beckman or Kollowitz, or find a bright red surface that wasn't a fire extinguisher or an emergency exit. Though human kind may not be able to bear very much reality does everyone wish to be anaesthetised against it? The attainment of health is the attainment of a condition of wholeness. In the words of C G Jung -

> 'The labours of the doctor as well as the quest of the patient
> are directed towards that hidden and as yet unmanifest
> "whole" man, who is at once the greater and the future man.
> But the right way to wholeness is made up, unfortunately, of
> fateful detours and wrong turnings. It is a longissima via, not
> straight but snakelike, a path that unites the opposites in the
> manner of the guiding caduceus, a path whose labyrinthine
> twists and turns are not lacking in terrors. It is on this
> longissima via that we meet with those experiences which
> are said to be "inaccessible". Their inaccessibility really
> consists in the fact that they cost us an enormous amount of
> effort; they demand the very thing we most fear, namely the
> "wholeness" which we talk about so glibly and which lends
> itself to endless theorising, though in actual life we give it the
> widest possible berth. '

Psychology and Alchemy, C G Jung

THE ARTIST AS PRODUCER
Su Braden

It is interesting and sad that there has never been a conference in this country called 'art for need'. The question, 'is there a need for art?' would not generally be seen even to make use of the same meaning of the word 'need'. I'm presuming it implies 'designing to meet necessity' - as opposed to 'designing to create necessity'. It is a functional and social proposition. But applied to art, the word need is generally assumed in the West to be detached from all base considerations and to apply to the more esoteric requirements of the soul.

Now I realise that I could be accused of producing false categories - a great deal of design is esoteric as well as functional and it is possible to argue, and in fact, it will be one aspect of my proposition, that the spiritual need for art is as great as the physical and spiritual need that exists for design. I argue though, that the separation of art and design is in itself a totally false one produced by pressures of Capitalism.

It is clear that both art and design in the West are dominated by the notion of their separate state - one the non-functional, the other the functional. This in spite of the fact that, as long ago as 1934, Walter Banjamin delivered a paper entitled 'The Author as producer.' In it he sets out the case for, in his instance, the writer being responsible for not only producing a work of literary merit, but the social structure in which the work itself may be meaningfully read - taking responsibility for the distribution and dissemination of his ideas.

Now if we are set on maintaining the status quo - none of this side of things need concern us; we make our work as artists or designers, and we use the appropriate channels to get them distributed. The question I wish to ask is - how 'appropriate' are these channels? (I will concern myself principally with the role of art and artists but most of what I will be proposing is equally applicable to design and designers.)

The notion that art need not be socially relevant is probably unique to Western society. In tribal society all art, from costume, pots and ritual dance to house decoration, masks and objects, has social significance, not just to certain elite sections of the tribe but to the life-style of the whole. The 'Third World' has shown by the examples of Cuba, Chile and Angola, that in those situations art is seen as the vanguard of progressive thought, as one of the media of consciousness-raising, necessary to achieve self-determination. Even in totalitarian Eastern Europe, art, whether social-realist and principally illustrational, or avant garde and subversive, is universally accepted (or persecuted) for being meaningful.

Today, we are slowly awakening to the pressures behind the production and promotion of the abstract expressionist movement in painting. A form of painting without images which was so highly acceptable to post-McCarthy America that the CIA financed the

American pavillion at the Venice Biennale (circa 1956). We may well wonder whether an art which is irrelevant to the vast majority of the population is necessary. But, at the same time, we should perhaps be asking ourselves whether in a world where most societies see art as an extension of their social codes, there is not a gaping vacuum in contemporary Western culture, a symptom of which is the fact that only the rich would feel a real sense of loss if there were no 'high' art at all.

The real issue is in fact probably this: that 'high art' in Capitalist society, far from setting standards and acting as a stimulus to the popular arts, has become a commodity, divorced of any broader social relevance than its cost. There are many complex contributing factors to the continuing acceptance by both artists and people, of lack of need for social relevance in art:

> Artists in particular are educated away from such a concept.
> The education of artists in all media reinforces the concept
> of a recognisable hierarchy pertaining to 'excellence'. This
> notion of 'accepted' standards does not encourage debate about
> the economic and social structure surrounding those standards.
> The education of artists is more often an education towards
> certain formalised notions of art. It is prejudiced against
> breaking down the 'traditional' ie 'commercial' structures
> into which such art forms are designed to fit.

> Art education in schools trains a public that will see 'high art'
> as a commodity that it cannot afford, or, very often, under-
> stand. It is very seldom compared to other essential skills,
> as an accessible medium of expression (like reading words or
> reading music).

> Patronage and funding play a part too. How much does
> patronage control the forms the arts take in the West? State
> patronage echoes the commodity based system set up by
> private patronage and is in fact often run or advised by the
> same people. This system closes the debate on the selection
> of art, and in doing so, further removes art from public
> participation in its creation.

Looking at contemporary art and artists in the light of these influences we feel secure in asking - is it now possible to abandon a universal standard of excellence? For what is 'excellence' without participation? Isn't it time we examined the myth of standards 'maintained' from the top? We feel that an aesthetic can also be meaningful and useful.

The only true criterion for judging art is the level of experience it offers to those who participate in it. Creativity cannot be seen as simply one person producing for another - active and passive - but must be seen as an act resulting from the social context in which it was produced.

So it is that most bourgeois art has little meaning for the working class and vice versa. It is absurd for the 'socialist' artist to attempt to effect or comment on the comparative wage scales of shop girls and factory workers in the Institute of Contemporary Arts in the Mall.

The structure of Capitalism produces the impossibility of a functional art.   Under
Capitalism there is a mutually destructive relationship between art and design which
can be seen brutally expressed in the way millions of people are housed.   Design can
be seen in this situation as reinforcing the positioning of art in a commodity base.
Architects for instance, who take (or are forced to take) a view of design work as
simply exchange of their ideal values for a certain standard of living (and who in any
case have, in most traditional work situations, little possibility of breaking down the
means of production), may be instrumental in preventing self-expression by the
inhabitants of the dwellings they design.   The fact that art and design are seen as
divorced from the means of production, introduces the kind of alienation in the West
which isolates artistic expression in the commercial galleries, theatres and concert
halls and design in chic drawing offices - rendering both socially powerless.

AFTER THE OIL BOOM - DESIGN FOR A SERVICE CENTRE

Brian Boylan, Mike Fletcher and Keith Priest

If the oil prospectors hit it rich in the Celtic Sea, the position of the small coastal towns and villages on shore could well be the same as those on Scotland's east coast some six years ago. For the fishing villages there the question was, and still is, what are the costs to the community of the move from being a fishing community to an oil village? Are the jobs and the revenues, both urgently needed, worth the disruption and environmental mayhem that follows? In the light of such problems, it is notoriously difficult these days for oil prospectors to get planning permission for shore bases in Scotland. The oil developers confront local authorities, national priorities are invoked, tempers rise. There may, however, be a different way of approaching this whole problem.

A building design team from the design consultancy Wolff Olins has produced a conceptual scheme (shown in deliberately anonymous form) relating to a particular supply base on the east coast, chosen because it is typical of its kind. It is not a concrete proposal but a drawing board exercise, worked out according to a concept which can not only respond to the industry's needs, but can without compromise be effectively integrated into the locality.

The team started with two points. Firstly, where on-shore bases have been built they tend to exist in a vacuum which increases the isolation between the locality, the company and its employees. Secondly, shore bases are short-lived: supply bases for exploration rigs can expect to stay in business for a maximum of fifteen years, perhaps as little as five. So the solution proposes structures which would be compatible with the local environment and be demountable or convert to other uses.

The chosen base has $6,500m^2$ of warehousing with $3,600m^2$ of office space on reclaimed land, adjacent to a small traditional east coast village.

Following a brief analysis of the requirements of the base, it was decided that the office element could be contained in small scale units and that the warehousing could be a minimal demountable shelter.

The usual kind of warehouse used on current bases of this type is unnecessarily enclosed from the point of view of stored goods and inadequately serviced from the point of view of those who work there. It is an out-of-doors environment, calling for cold weather clothing and heated cabs on the goods-handling vehicles. Furthermore, since most of the goods-handling activity actually occurs outside on the wharf, more attention needs to be paid to localised personal comforts (protective clothing, heated truck cabs, etc). The solution chosen was an off-the-peg, easily demountable, unit tensile structure laid on a 10m x 10m grid.

The office space, however, could not be included in this treatment. It seemed that this element would provide the integration with the existing village and as such could be of a more permanent form.

An irregular line of 'office' terraced housing which fitted in with the existing style of housing in the village was designed to act as the office element. This could eventually become actual housing and, in the immediate future, would provide the pattern for any future development, industrial or housing.

Between the warehouse element and the office terraces, there would be a demountable structure which would carry services to the 'housing shells' and provide the horizontal and vertical communications between them.

But the community gains more than just housing possibilities. The office terrace worl as a sympathetic screen for the camouflaged industrial area behind. The client can hide his non-community activities and bring forward certain sympathetic street activit (company post office, cafe/canteen) helping to soften the traditionally hard company/ public interface.

Finally when the oil men leave, taking with them the tent and the demountable servicir structure, the local people are left with three assets: housing and housing 'shells', established street facilities inherited from the company, and the potential for any number of extra street facilities, using the office units in much the same way as the company did.

This scheme is only a hypothesis, invoking many detailed ideas which may be inapplic able on any other site. But the approach can be generalised and perhaps the existence of this one scheme will demonstrate to all that there are ways of integrating the new industries.

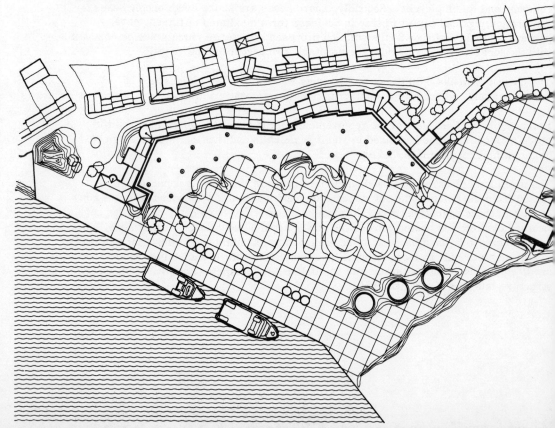

LE DEMESURABLE
Bernard Lassus

(M Lassus' paper, which deals with the role of the imagination in the man-made
environment, was delivered in French with an extempore translation by Jean Liedloff
and numerous slides. The following text is taken partly from a translation prepared
by Françoise Ferly and partly from the French text of the catalogue of M Lassus'
recent exhibition in Paris. In it a number of terms cannot be translated literally
without confusion. They are therefore left in the original French. Ed.)

In what follows I wish to contrast what I call the 'Démesurable' (lit: immeasurable),
a notion which may remain slightly foggy, with the so-called 'rational' which, by
striving for precision and efficiency and denying a sensitive or sensuous approach, is
choking our environment.

In 1961 I was engaged on a study of colour in Corsican villages and noticed that besides
choosing the colours of their houses and laying out paths and plants, certain inhabitants
create special figurative objects. I found fabulous animals such as a red cement
dragon with long white teeth and a yellow spotted green snake with a wire tongue. They
reminded me of postman Cheval's Ideal Palace and Raymond Isidore's house 'Picassiette'
and I wondered whether these marvels had eclipsed other examples. Nobody knew
much about these objects and there are no books on the subject so I decided to organise
a survey in areas where the phenomena might occur. I formed teams of 'paysagistes'
(landscapists) and 'plasticiens' (plastic artists) to search the suburbs of Paris, Bethune,
Marseille and some towns in the East of France. Prompted by the discovery that this
type of phenomenon is most developed in the arrangement of front gardens, we chose
to look at the suburban detached house and that special zone between the street boundary
and the house front. Several years and thousands of miles later our survey documents
many examples of these 'environmental interventions'.

The passion with which certain householders, both tenant and owner, transform their
environment is remarkable. Their interventions develop from the tiniest areas: a
wall, a window surround, a balcony or even a window box. Despite the most discour-
aging circumstances they cover the walls with motifs, they make little objects, they
plant flowers in profusion. Incredible landscapes shatter their few square metres
into imaginary spaces. A deer or pheasant suggests a forest - M Pecqueur, an
ex-miner, says of his painted cement creatures, 'The animals are the forest'. A
lighthouse in a pond or two boats on the eaves evoke the immensity of the ocean. The
'Tour de France' races across the bridge at Tancarville over a two metre pond. Popeye
with a telescope, all in painted cement, spies a stone ship loaded with seasonal flowers.
The difference in scale between the life-size Popeye and the six-metre boat implies the
distance that requires the spyglass. The actual scale of the paving is of course out
of place in this seascape, so a mermaid is arranged to spring from the flagstones
behind the boat. The display is all the more forceful for lack of space and the

miniaturisation of some or all of the elements creates space in the imagination.

Taking a closer look at M Charles Pecqueur's garden we come upon a hare, landing
gracefully after an easy leap; a few metres further on we find a tortoise, legs and
neck strained in a final effort to reach a hoop marked in large letters with the word
'BUT' (goal in French). Of course only a recognition of the fable allows such precise
description of the animals' postures and establishes their relationship although they
are some distance apart. In fact the position of each shows that we are witness to
the exact moment when the hare can no longer win, no matter what he does. Given
such a well known fable interpretation is simple, but other cases are less obvious.
When the 'artist' has in mind a little known relationship or one he has invented himself,
the scenes can be very difficult to understand however realistic the various elements.
In these cases we can only identify the most familiar objects - the figurative, the
typical, the most easily identified - a rabbit, a boat, a dwarf, a castle. Isolated
from their context by this process of recognition these elements are identified by
friends and passers-by as independent objects. Their curiosity can generate commercial demand and our 'artist' begins to make hares, tortoises and snakes for sale,
quite independent of their original purpose. In order to distinguish these manufacturers
of objects from those who use them as parts of their landscapes, I call the latter
'habitants-paysagistes' (landscaper-occupiers).

During his eighteen-year term as mayor M Pecqueur also undertook the embellishment
of a roundabout in front of the Town Hall. With the help of the road mender he
illustrated the tale of Snow White and the Seven Dwarfs with a surround of walls and
stone arches. He even planned water and coloured light effects accompanied by the
music from the Disney film. But unhappily the election of a new town council halted
the project. The whole thing was destroyed and thrown on the council tip. Only a
few arches remain. Deeply afflicted by this, M Pecqueur has since developed the
story of his island in a series of murals in his own garden that trace the growth of the
project. Snow White herself was the only figure to escape destruction. She now stands
at the end of the plot behind his house, gazing forlornly over the neighbouring gardens.

This rejection in the name of good taste recurs in a garden featuring a three-and-a-
half metre high wooden Eiffel Tower. The 'artist', another miner, entered the local
garden competition. He was reprimanded by the jury for his windmill made of used
tyres, several wooden birds, a well, a plastic salad bowl tortoise and the Eiffel
Tower: to win a prize these objects ought to be suppressed in favour of lawn, hedges
and natural flowers. Shocked and uncomprehending but none the less ambitious for
a prize, the miner has consequently removed a few objects year by year. But the
Eiffel Tower is still there.

M Sulek on the other hand is indifferent to the approval of the jury and has developed
special links between his model buildings and his geometrical layout. The clumps of
flowers that surround his models - a windmill and the Bruay-en-Artois town hall -
are their own landscapes in miniature. The windmill is on a wooded hillock. The
town hall adjoins the garden path as if facing a street. Furthermore the flower basin
of old tyres (turned inside out and painted white) is seen, from a specially placed bench,
as the foreground of an elaborate trompe-l'oeil perspective, with the town hall and
its park in the middle distance and the windmill on a remote hilltop. All this in a

front garden seven metres deep.

Similar manifestations turn up in the work of 'serious' contemporary artists such as
the poet Ian Hamilton Finlay. In the garden of his Scottish farm house there is a
pool with a bird table in the form of an aircraft carrier. The birds which come to eat
the crumbs on the flight deck are aeroplanes, the pond the sea. Nearby a sign warns:
'Do not feed the boats'.

A photograph sent to me by Finlay, from an exhibition he presented in Reno Nevada,
provided the key to one of the most puzzling combinations of objects that we had found
in the seaside town of Les Sables d'Ollone. We had found in addition to a windmill and
a mannikin-pis, a red painted submarine on a two metre post and a pair of yachts on
the eaves of the house. Finlay's photograph showed another submarine, 'No 571',
ploughing through the evergreen foliage of a thicket of Western Cedar - the movement
of the branches in the wind being the motion of the waters of the deep, their rustling
the sound of the waves. So the yachts on the eaves at Les Sables d'Ollone make the
vertical plane of the house front represent the depth of the ocean. The red submarine
is full fathom five under the sea.

These metaphorical landscapes invoke the 'démesurable'. They also underline the
failure of 'official' culture to keep up with folk 'art'. Their similarities, whether in
Paris, Edinburgh or Stockholm, reinforce my belief in their genuine character and
contemporary value.

The powerful physical presence of these creations demands a study of the relationship
between the original landscape and the interpolations, between the context and the
objects, or as it were, the substrate and the insert. The 'habitant-paysagiste' seeks
a contrast with his surroundings, some type of luxury interwoven with bright colours,
textures, lights, sounds and the movement of water. The 'professional' method
however is to integrate, that is to blend the interpolations into the landscape. But this
integration tends to narrow the range of options for further interpolation. Each insert
establishes the new context for further manipulation, but these well mannered additions
reinforce the established character of a landscape and tend to fix it. It is only when
the environment develops a richness of contrasts that it will be able to accommodate
the unexpected. It is the differences, not the similarities that enhance our surrounding
This richness of contrasts is my fundamental working hypothesis.

Everyone elaborates the landscape for himself by identifying certain meanings and
relationships. This elaboration goes far beyond the realm covered by the purely
'plastic' arts. For objects act in the landscape according to the meaning they convey.
A church tower for instance fits quite happily into the scenery despite its size while
a water tower of similar bulk appears foreign and aggressive.

This uneasiness at the disparities of scale in our modern world is expressed by our
clumsy terminology - 'environment', 'urban agglomeration' etc. We are unable to
think in terms of whole landscapes; we see only collections of objects.

In our recent study of an overall scheme for the appearance of Housing Sector II at the
new town of Marne-la-Vallée (near Paris) we developed a novel relationship between

professional designers and the occupiers. Certain professionals advocate occupier
participation in the design and fitting out of housing as a means to developing a sense
of pride and 'belonging'. In my view a sense of belonging arises not from do-it-yourself
building but from the use of leisure. If people are compelled to build their own houses
(particularly if there are economic pressures as well) it is a restriction not a freedom.
True, the elaboration of standard structures is often prompted by pride in belonging,
together with a do-it-yourself instinct - but no occupant should be bound to act in this
way. The professionals should solve the utilitarian and economic problems in such
a way that the occupants can develop their sense of belonging in their leisure time.
After all they may want to mess about in the house or potter in the garden but they
might prefer to go fishing, smoke a cigarette or just day-dream. The 'habitant-
paysagiste' works from choice not compulsion. His need is for the needless.

So our aim at Marne-la-Vallée was to provide richness in the landscape base,
independent of the intervention of the occupants. Our studies had shown that the
diversity of meaning we were after, could be provided within a dominant theme of a
plastic nature (such as colour) for a cluster of 750 dwellings (La Maurellette in
Marseille). But it cannot be done for a larger group (like the 2,000 at Quetigny les
Dijons), however wide and contrasting the range of colours. From our examination
of the 'habitant-paysagiste' we had identified a large range of different activities
that produced the diversity we sought; decoration, the elaboration of ties between
houses and setting, the dislocation of space by miniaturisation. These and other
methods were applied to zones of 750 dwellings and each zone was given a dominant
theme, say 'colour' to distinguish it from the neighbouring zones where 'vegetation',
'texture' or even 'light' might be dominant. In this way each zone can be varied in
itself while contrasting with its neighbours. You will note that I have avoided the
word complexity because it is the quality of the result, not its intellectual subtlety,
that counts. The complexity we seek cannot be achieved by complication.

The term dominant of course implies that several elements can be used. The planner
will for instance support his 'texture' dominant with colour, light and plant life -
accenting the dominant by contrast. The secondary characteristics are not excluded
in favour of the dominant. After all, the object is to enrich not impoverish the visual
heirarchy.

Our aim is not to make rules about the appearance of the environment but to stimulate
investigation within the dominant themes - to replace abstract architecture by an
architecture with a more direct and sensual visual presence. Why should the occupant
and their visitors be bothered with a visual abstraction of the technique of building
that only really interests the originator or specialist? Why not use the visual meaning
of building - its 'sense', to create a sensual and sensitive environment?

Our proposal is an alternative to the accumulation of negative attitudes that is most
often met within these fields. Usually each construction grows and mutilates the
character of its surroundings; the highway drives in front of the house blocks, a silo
desecrates a valley. Space is felt more and more as a continuum of fittings; the
global landscape is only quasi-permanent. Worse still it is impossible to escape -
to 'go West young Man.' '

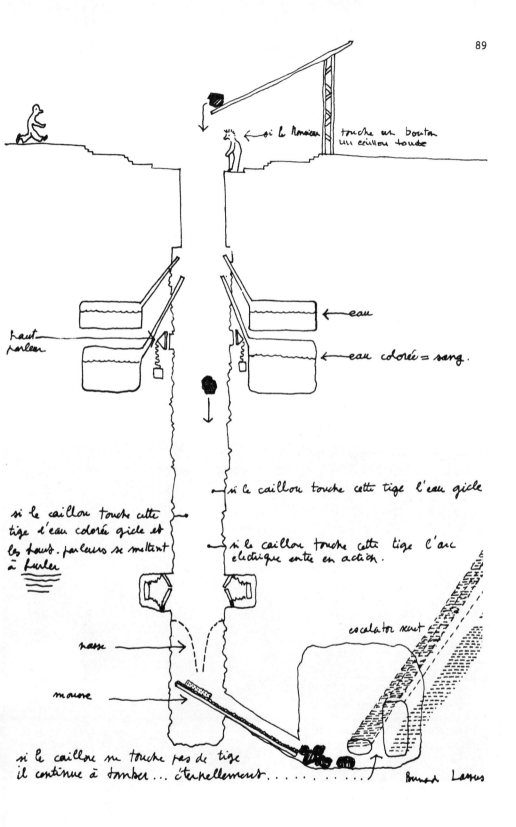

si le Monsieur touche un bouton
un caillou tombe

← eau

haut
parleur

← eau colorée = sang.

si le caillou touche cette tige l'eau gicle

si le caillou touche cette
tige l'eau colorée gicle et
les haut.parleurs se mettent
à hurler

si le caillou touche cette tige l'arc
electrique entre en action.

escalator roux

nasse

mouve

si le caillou ne touche pas de tige
il continue à tomber... éternellement..........

Bernard Lassus

We no longer have landscapes whose fulcrum of understanding is immeasurably deep.
The aeroplane reduces the sea to a pond. Pollution reduces the pond to a cesspool.
Only a tempest can restore the 'démesurable'. Nowadays Petit Poucet (Tom Thumb)
can't get lost in a giant-infested forest when the birds eat the trail of crumbs he has
laid to mark his way. Everything is measured on an all too human scale. Too many
landscapes are finite.

The issue in question is the confrontation of classical measure with the primitive.
It is no longer enough to contrast the finite (the cottage or castle) with the infinite
(the forest). Nor can we rely on compromises like the manicuring of trees to mediate
between the man-made and natural woods. We must use the elaboration of systems of
relationship to stretch finite objects to the infinite. Nowadays all that you'll find at
the bottom of the garden is the wire link fence that marks the boundary. The fairies
and the forests have escaped through the mesh.

Direct contact with the primitive, the savage, is now virtually impossible. Darkness
and light offer one of the few outlets left. Artificial light can dematerialise surfaces;
transparency and reflection can induce ambiguities between appearance and reality.
Take the old example of the well. Which of us has not dropped a pebble into the
impenetrable darkness of a well to judge its depth from the splash or clink at the
bottom? Well, suppose there is no sound and the pebble falls on and on and on ...

This tearing of objects from their physical parameters is what I call the 'démesurable'.

DESIGNING FOR NEED - RADIO TALK

Peter Lloyd Jones

It was clear from the title - 'Design for Need' - that the conference was making a bid for a slogan to put at the masthead of a new ideology of design - a new set of beliefs that would not only inspire designers in practice, but which could revitalise design education. Now is certainly the moment, for it is blindingly obvious that 'functionalism' - the framework of ideas and images that has under-pinned the last fifty years of the mainstream effort of modern design - has collapsed. The modernist slogans of 'ornament is crime', 'less is more', 'fitness for use', that set the design world on fire fifty years ago, led to the assertion that efficiency and practicality must be best served by a particular kind of visual language - a language which tended to ruthless simplicity. The visual economy implicit in functionalism has produced a brutal simplification of our environment which is being rejected everywhere, not least by students of design. And so into this philosophical and aesthetic vacuum steps 'Design for Need'.

What then is the idea behind 'Design for Need'? As a slogan it aims to tie together the efforts of a particular group of designers who reject the idea that design should be, as it usually is now, 'a secondary activity responding to the needs of governmental and industrial organisations who are largely responsible for the initiation of design and the formulation of briefs'. They claim that many human needs, even some of the most important ones, are ignored by industry and government alike. The problems they want to solve simply never turn up in the briefs they are given. These designers, who see themselves as itinerant problem-solvers to society at large, feel that designers themselves must initiate design activity in direct response to their own perception of human needs.

But is this in fact the alternative philosophy we have been waiting for? I don't think so. But before I say why, I should like to mention its ancestry.

There is, firstly, and particularly in this country, a long tradition of social criticism among designers and theoreticians. No doubt 'Design for Need' drew inspiration from this source. But there is a more recent upsurge of social criticism among designers which arose directly from a disenchantment with their particular role in the prod-uctive process of modern technological society.

One designer still whirling in the older ethical tradition (and a disciple of Buckminster Fuller) is the American, Victor Papanek. He preaches a Utopian view of the possibil-ities of the designer himself coming in to sort out the mess. In his book 'Design for the Real World' published in 1972, he has proposed an 'Alternative' agenda of design projects, an agenda aimed at tackling the failures and omissions of previous design. Papanek's message is 'Only if we get down to it problem by problem can we still hope to survive as a society. If society won't give the lead then we, as designers, must'.

His book is in many ways original and full of practical suggestions which have had great influence.   Fittingly he was one of the main speakers at the conference which undoubtedly owed much to him.

In the event, the conference and exhibition assembled a large range of disparate projects, projects ranging from home-made methane generators and organic gardening to the artistic decoration of bleak ('functional') hospital interiors. On the global scale, the possibilities for revolution inherent in a universal design education which would enable everyone to 'do their own thing' were mooted; but it was in reality the small-scale, local enterprises that stuck in the mind.

Projects such as street theatres, community workshops and co-operative educational enterprises among children in deprived areas testified to the selfless dedication of artists and designers invariably working on shoestring budgets at great personal cost. At a theoretical level, however, it proved impossible to go from the success of the particular to define any general policies for action by designers in the face of the larger predicaments which face mankind: the population explosion, the resource crisis, the over-production of waste or, for that matter, the alienation of those caught up in the self-same assembly-lines our industrial designers are taught to design for. This failure was inevitable, I think. For there is surely a difficulty inherent in the concept of 'need' which stands in the way of it being applied in any systematic fashion.

In fact, it is very difficult to know what a 'need' actually is. Marx seems to have regarded men's needs as biological drives which were real, objective and measurable, and as such susceptible to scientific observation and understanding. 'Desires' or 'wants' were the outer expression of these inner realities. The snag is that you can really only get directly at what a man desires. What is available to observation, only provides an account of his alleged wants.

'Need' therefore in practice becomes an abstract deduction or inference from a consensus of desires or wants. These may, of course, have a certain objectivity. Market research or statistical sampling can reveal an average desire or want. But even those are not very stable since they can be intensified or even created by advertising or propaganda. Moreover, it often happens that different people's desires conflict and it is necessary to adjudicate on which desires are to be regarded as legitimate. What this makes clear is that need is not an empirical notion based on sense observation. On the contrary it conceals a moral judgement behind the apparently purely factual facade. Nor are these judgements an easy matter for often enough a man's desires may conflict with what someone else thinks he needs.

To cope with these paradoxes we might have to bring in Freud and the notion of 'unconscious needs' - which are certainly not easy things to design for. It is true that one can attempt to sort out 'basic' or 'essential' needs from the rest, but here again, the subjective nature of even such evaluations can be seen from the perennial difficulty in defining a minimum standard of living. One man's 'needs' are another man's 'luxuries' - and they all change all the time.

And so, 'Design for Need' is a philosophy that makes sense only in certain limited

and simple conditions. At the margin of human survival, biological need is clear cut.
The dramatisation of this meaning of need, no doubt, inspired the many 'survival'
projects which were presented at the conference. These arose from an interest in
extreme environmental conditions (capsule projects for climatic extremes) or from
catastrophe situations (for example, disaster housing for earthquake zones). By a
slight extension from this limiting case of biological survival there is the current
interest in design for the limbless and the disabled and beyond that again the elderly
or the sick, or the young, or the pregnant. In such situations of manifest biological
handicap, what is a necessary condition for a minimum level of comfort and mobility
is obvious and 'need' in this sense determines design solutions which overwhelm other
considerations. But once again as we try to extend the idea of 'need' to the more
general sense of well-being at a psychological or sociological level, we find that it
simply disintegrates as any useful objective criterion for selecting design problems.

You see that the question of who decides what really is a 'need' is one of critical
importance. If 'needs' are to be part of the designer's brief then one must surely
agree that at the very least - to adapt a phrase - 'Design is too important to be left
to designers'.

This was a message that came out over and over again from those who had actually
lived and worked in areas of famine or disaster or of gross social deprivation in city
slums.

> 'Go and live with the people. Work with them - and then see
> what you can do to help. If you try to help from outside you
> are unlikely to succeed and you may inadvertently do more
> harm than good. For the deprived are, as individuals, people
> just like you. Their desires are just as diverse, contradictory
> and conflicting as your own. Their societies are as subtle and
> complex, as unjust and intractable to the armchair social
> engineer as your own.'

But to do this is precisely to engage in the social and political life of the community.
Designers can take part in the initiation of briefs by society but as citizens not as
designers. They cannot by-pass this reality - merely pointing to 'needs', for in
practice, the resolution of differing judgements of 'need' simply is the never-ending
life of the market place and of the political process. What then can designers, working
within the tradition of our colleges of art and design, contribute that is uniquely their
own? Something that cannot be done better elsewhere by similarly socially committed
groups of engineers, planners or economists?

Is it not the capacity to demonstrate that beauty can be created anywhere? 'Beautiful'
was not a word I heard much during the conference. But one had only to regard the
ugliness of flown-in aluminium earthquake shelters and compare this with the beauty
of indigenous native tents (probably equally 'functional' by the way) to see what was
missing. It would be all too easy to let loose another flood of visual barbarism amid
the crash programmes generated from a well-meaning but naive concentration on
'needs' as if these were facts, not values.

Beauty as a value is universally exhibited even in the poorest societies in other cultures. It exists not as a by-product of the practical but because it is treasured as such and scarce resources are diverted to provide it. If the functionalist was often purveying a covert (and ultimately disastrous) aesthetic, the 'Design for Need' man can easily end up forgetting aesthetics altogether amid the urgencies of 'problem - solving'. Some indeed reject this entirely in a contemptuous puritanism.

When Papanek's book was published in this country, 'Design' magazine had the nice idea of asking Anthony Wedgwood Benn to review it. He ended his largely favourable review by making a point which reinforces my contention: he said, 'What Papanek needs is to make contact with some political philosophers or practitioners who also see themselves as problem-solvers. They would have a lot to talk about. ' Quite so. Perhaps this conference could provide a starting point for such a conversation. But I hope there will be a chance to discuss the beautiful together with the practical and the socially desirable. All those things in fact which the language of 'problem-solving for need' leaves out.

DESIGN FOR SOCIAL NEED - THE
LUCAS WORKERS' INITIATIVE
Mike Cooley

There are hosts of contradictions which underline the absurdities of our so-called technologically advanced society. Four of these contradictions are particularly relevant to what I have to say. Firstly there is the appalling gap that exists between that which technology could provide for society and that which it actually does. We have a level of sophistication in technology, such that we can produce Concord, yet we cannot provide enough simple heating systems to protect old age pensioners from hypothermia. In the winter of 1975-6, 980 died of the cold in the London area alone. We have senior automotive engineers who sit in front of visual display units working interactively to optimise the configuration of car bodies such that they are aero-dynamically stable at 120 mph when the average speed of traffic through New York is now 6.2 mph. (It was in fact 11 mph at the turn of the century when vehicles were horse drawn.) We have sophisticated communication systems which can send messages round the world in nano-seconds yet it now takes longer to send a letter from Washington than it did in the days of the stage coach.

The second contradiction is the manner in which our society is incapable of using its most precious asset - that is its people with their ingenuity, their skill, their energy and their creativity. We have now in Britain one and a quarter million people out of work. There are thousands of engineers in the dole queue when we urgently need cheap, effective and safe transport systems for our cities. There are thousands of electricians out of work when we need cheap, urban heating systems and we have thousands of building workers out of a job when something like seven million people still live in slums in Britain.

The third contradiction is the myth that computerisation, automation and the use of advanced technological equipment will free human beings from the soul destroying, back-breaking tasks and leave them free to engage in creative work. The perception of my members and millions of workers in industrial countries is that in many instances the opposite is the case.

And fourthly there is the growing hostility of society to science and technology as at present applied. If one goes to a gathering where there are artists, journalists and writers and you say that you are a technologist they treat you as some latter-day ya-hoo, to misquote Swift, and treat you as though you specified that rust should be sprayed on to car bodies before the paint is applied, that all commodities should be enclosed in non-recycleable containers and that every large scale plant you produce is designed specifically to pollute the air and the rivers. Indeed many young and able sixth-formers will not now study science and technology because they see the way they are misapplied in our society.

All of these four contradictions have impacted themselves upon the workers in

95

Lucas Aerospace over the past five years: we do work on major parts of Concord; we
have experienced structural unemployment; and we experience day by day the growing
public hostility to science and technology. Lucas Aerospace was formed in the late
1960's when parts of Lucas Aerospace interests took over sections of GEC, AEI and a
number of other small companies. It was clear that the company would engage in a
rationalisation programme along the lines of that already established by Arnold
Wienstock in GEC. In order that one plant could not be set against the other we built
a combine committee which represented all workers in Lucas Aerospace. This body
is still unique in the British Trade Union Movement, in that it links together the
highest level technologists with the semi-skilled workers on the shop floor. There is
therefore a unique cross fertilisation between the analytical power of the scientist and
technologist on the one hand - and on the other, and perhaps much more importantly,
the direct class sense and understanding of those on the workshop floor. As structural
unemployment began to affect us we looked about at the manner in which other workers
were resisting it. We too were engaged in partial sit-ins, in preventing the transfer
of work from one plant to another and the host of other industrial tactics which have
been developed over the past few years. But we saw that when society doesn't want
the products that you make, the morale of a work force making those items very
quickly declines. We therefore evolved the idea of a campaign for the right to work on
socially useful products.

We prepared 180 letters which described precisely the work force we had available -
all fourteen thousand of them, the machine tools, the equipment, the research labora-
tories and the design capabilities. Though we wrote to many of the leading authorities,
institutions, universities and organisations who over the years had stated that they
believed that technology should be applied in a more responsible fashion, we received
only three replies that were in any way concrete or specific. So we devised a relatively
simple questionnaire to find out what our own members felt they should be making.
As a result of this questionnaire we got 150 ideas of alternative products on which we
may work. The net result of all this was a proposal which we now call the Lucas
Aerospace Workers Corporate Plan. It is an extensive document, running to six
volumes, each of some 200 pages. It includes very detailed, technical and specific
proposals, as well as setting out clearly the underlying philosophy of the plan as a
whole. I will describe briefly some of the products selected.

One of the major areas we looked at was medical equipment. Lucas Aerospace already
makes pacemakers and a number of kidney machines. In fact the Lucas Aerospace
kidney machine won the Design Council's award last year for medical equipment. The
unfortunate thing is that our company regards the kidney machine as incompatible with
its product range and attempted to sell it to an international monopoly in Switzerland.
The work force took direct action against this and prevented the company selling it.
There is an acute shortage of kidney machines in Britain, and every year some three
thousand are allowed, as they so nicely put it, 'to decline', ie to die. Part of our
corporate plan is for a simplified version of this machine and a demand that the
production of kidney machines should be increased by forty per cent. We regard it as
absurd that the skilled workers who can produce and design this kind of equipment
are being thrown into the dole queue where the tax-payer has to find them approximate
forty pounds a week, when for a little more they could be producing commodities
which, even if they were not regarded as being profitable, are certainly socially usefu

Another medical product was a device known as a hobcart. Some of our members at the Wolverhampton plant designed this after visiting a local centre for children with spina bifida. They were hoffified to see that the only way the children could move was by crawling on the floor. So they designed a vehicle for them which not only helped them to move about but was also of therapeutic value. It was designed by a multidisciplinary team which included medical practitioners, physiotherapists and health workers. It was an enormously enriching experience to work in this multidisciplinary team.

Also in the medical field we are talking about devices which would help the blind to 'see', a heat exchanger which would maintain blood at an optimum temperature during operations and a small portable life-support system which could be used in ambulances until patients could be got to the main life-support system in a hospital.

A second area we are considering in great detail is equipment for alternative energy sources. We have designed integrated house sheeting systems including solar-collectors and heat-pumps. We have even made arrangements with local councils that these could be used. (We don't like the idea of this kind of equipment being available only to people in their architect-built houses where they are a sort of sophisticated play thing. We believe that they should really serve the community.) With our considerable skills in aerodynamics we have devised a number of large scale wind-generators. There is nothing new about wind-generators but ours have a unique rotor speed control system. At a more complex level we are proposing the development of a range of gaseous hydrogen fuel cells because our present sources of energy are finite and are being exhausted at an exponential rate. Another area is in the field of oceanatics. We believe that during the coming years very much greater use will be made of the sea bed. Despite the highly irresponsible fashion in which human beings have used the one third of the earth's surface which is above sea level, we think that there will be a socially responsible marine agriculture. It is our view that a whole range of crops will be grown on the sea bed and we are proposing a number of submersible vehicles that will be capable of sowing and harvesting these remotely.

We have proposed a whole range of equipment for developing countries. One of the units we have in mind is an auxiliary power-pack. At the moment when our gin-and-tonic sales-brigade go out, they attempt to convince those in developing countries that power supplies should be met by purchasing a separate unit for each requirement. We are proposing a universal power-pack for developing countries. A basic prime-mover, a combustion engine capable of running on conventional fuel or methane, would drive a series of power output heads where the speed could be changed by a specially designed gearbox. The unit would be capable of producing electricity or of producing compressed air or pumping water or even providing high pressure hydraulics.

In the volume of our report dealing with transport systems we propose a range of products from simple auxiliary devices to complete alternative vehicles. At the lower end of the scale we've suggested that dynamometers (which we now use to test the load on aircraft generators) should be redesigned so as to make them suitable for use as auxiliary breaking systems for cars, coaches and trains. Only ten per cent of the coaches in Britain are fitted with safety devices of this kind. The tragic Yorkshire coach crash last year might not have occurred had retarders been fitted. We have extended the idea by proposing electronic control systems that slow a coach or train to a gradual but complete standstill if the driver collapses. We emphasise that this would only happen in the event of a driver failure. It is not our intention to automate drivers or any other workers out of existence. As a prime mover of vehicles of all kinds we are proposing that the internal combustion engine and the high-torque electric motor could be linked. A small internal combustion engine, running constantly at optimum revs (it will be at a very high temperature as we circulate the exhaust gases in a manifold on the outside), would drive a generator to charge a stack of batteries that operate the electric motors. Technologists will immediately recognise that this combines two opposites; the high torque characteristics of the electric motor with the opposite characteristics of the internal combustion engine. We calculate that by doing this we could reduce fuel consumption by 50%, toxic emissions would be reduced by 80% and that the unit would be inaudible against a background noise of approximately fifty decibels at ten metres.

Now to produce equipment of this kind for the automotive industry would mean reversing the tendency in that industry to design for very high obsolescence. To make this power pack truly economically viable it would have to last from ten to fifteen years. So we have pointed out to our colleagues at Chrysler's that when confronted recently with the closure of their plant, their option was not between accepting the dole queue or continuing to produce rubbishy Chrysler cars. There were in fact other options open to them and we are greatly impressed by the steps they are now taking to consider these. Of course all this is a challenge to the underlying assumptions of the automotive industry. But it is a terrible waste of materials to produce cars of this throw-away kind.

The petrol driven private car also wastes huge quantities of fuel and energy - and indeed of the countryside in providing space for roads. We have therefore proposed a unique type of alternative public transport system in conjunction with the design staff at the North East London Polytechnic. It is a hybrid road-rail vehicle, capable firstly of travelling through our crowded cities as a coach running on conventional pneumatic tyres, and then turning off the road on to the railway network. Victorian engineers did a tremendous job in designing the network and rolling stock of the railways but they have the disadvantage of a metal rim running on a metal track, so that every shock is transmitted up through the superstructure. This means a very heavy springing system and a massive superstructure. We propose the reverse - a light and flexible structure running on pneumatic tyres.

The vehicle would be important not only in metropolitan Britain, but could be of great importance to developing countries (considerable interest is being shown by the Highland and Islands Development Board). The vehicle is capable of climbing inclines of 1 in 6, because of the friction between the metal track and the rubber tyre. Conventional railway systems are only capable of climbing a gradient of 1 in 80. The cost of the civil engineering required to flatten the mountains and fill up the valleys is truly enormous - the recent Tanzanian railway line built by the Chinese cost roughly £1 million per track-mile. For once it seems the thoughts of Mao Tse-tung were somewhat expensive. The cost of laying track for our vehicle would be a mere £20, 000 per track-mile and of course it could be used most successfully where railways already exist. Recent tests carried out on the East Kent Railway line have confirmed the viability of these proposals.

I should point out that these product ranges are only the first part of the corporate plan. Nevertheless, even in this first part there is the underlying assertion that ordinary working people have a right to decide what kind of products they should be producing and how they should be used. The second part of our corporate plan is perhaps even more important. In it we not only talk about producing different products but different ways of producing them.

Modern industry is characterised by narrow, fragmented, alienating tasks carried out at a frantic tempo. The skill of the worker is objectivised and built into the machine in such a fashion that he becomes a mere machine appendage. Those who are not mere appendages are displaced as industry becomes capital-intensive rather than labour intensive. Typical of this kind of equipment is the robotic device used at General Motors' plant in Lordstown in the United States. The worker takes the robot literally 'by the hand' (as the advertisement says) and guides it through the motions of spraying a car body. The robot records how it is done and objectivises the skill of the car body sprayer in the machine to confront him or her as an alien and opposite force. Car body spraying may not be a highly skilled job but I'm simply using it as a graphic example of objectivisation - in the real Marxist sense of the term.

At Lucas Aerospace we are not merely objecting to these tendencies, we have actually attempted to devise a range of teleheuric devices which would reverse it. They are basically systems which mimic human motions but where the human being is in control 'realtime all the time': by which we mean that the skill and talent of the human being is central to the control system - the human being is not displaced by the machine. This notion occurred to us in connection with efforts to devise a robotic device to maintain North Sea oil pipelines on the sea bed. Clearly such a device is desirable in that human beings should not be required to work in this incredibly hazardous environment. But such devices are severely limited. Think of the problems of programming a robot to recognise which way about a hexagon nut is (much less to put a spanner on it and tighten it up). Even the most complicated pattern recognition devices have only 10^3 intelligent units. Yet an ordinary human being has got 10^{14} synaptic connections. We have this frantic yearning to produce artificial intelligence systems when we've got one and a quarter million people degenerating in the dole queue whose pattern-recognition intelligence is infinitely greater than anything yet conceived. So we have designed a range of teleheuric devices for submarine work where the human being could work from the safety of a platform outside the hazardous environment feeding his or her intelligence to the actual point of work through the teleheuric device. The same kind of system could be used for coal mining where the coal miner could 'see' through television systems to actually 'work the face' but from a remote and safe environment, or in the field of fire-fighting where instead of requiring firemen to actually go into the fire they could use their skill and intelligence from a remote point to guide a teleheuric fire-fighting device.

We must also consider different means of producing products. We must move towards a 'people-centred' technology. We realise that this means challenging many of the assumptions of our society as at present constituted. When we talk about different production techniques we are not talking about 'group' technology as practiced for example at Volvo's in Sweden. Such job technology is really a purely manipulative arrangement in which, as one of our shop stewards put it, it is like putting somebody in

a cage and having a long discussion about the colour of the bars. Or as another shop
steward put it, it's like the advert for Kerrygold where they say 'Better Butter from
Contented Cows'. The so-called new production techniques are highly manipulative
affairs in which workers are made to believe that things are changing but the underlying
motive of the employer is simply to get workers working faster and if possible to
produce work of a slightly better quality or at least at a lower reject-rate. We have
always been told that science and technology would liberate us from soul destroying,
back-breaking tasks and leave us free to engage in more creative work. Yet if we
look objectively at some of the most technologically advanced firms in the world we
would see that the reverse is actually the case.

At Fiat in Italy, mentioned earlier by Victor Papanek, work is so grotesque and
fragmented and alienating that some 18% of the work force cannot face their jobs each
day. At Lordstown in the United States where they use the robotic device I described,
the workers actually sabotaged some of the equipment on the production line because
they felt completely alienated and subordinated to the equipment. Even in Sweden,
they have introduced so-called 'protected workshops' for people that cannot stand the
pressure of advanced technology. What a contradiction it is that people have actually
got to be protected from the very equipment which the pundits assured us would free
them from the worst aspects of advanced production. It is important that we recall
that these industrial systems were designed. There were designers callous and
indifferent enough to design equipment which does this to other human beings.

For instance, where the British Leyland Allegro bodies are pressed out, workers are
highly integrated with the production equipment itself. There is an official agreement
between one of the unions and the company, which illustrates my point. It deals with
the rest period in the complete work-cycle. The total rest period is 32.4 minutes
and it is made up of the following elements: trips to the lavatory - 1.62 minutes (not
1.6 or 1.7 - it is 1.62 - computer precise and the toilets are strategically located
close to the production line to make that possible); recovery from fatigue - 3.05 minutes
sitting down after standing too long - 65 seconds; from monotony - 32 seconds; and
so the grotesque litany goes on. I would like to point out what Robert Bogeslaw had to
say about designing man-machine systems:

> 'Our immediate concern let us remember is the exploitation
> of the operating-unit-approach to systems design - no matter
> what materials are used. We must take care to prevent this
> discussion degenerating into the single-sided analysis of the
> complex characteristics of one type of systems material -
> namely human-beings. What we need is an inventory of the
> manner in which human behaviour can be controlled and a
> description of some of the instruments which will help us to
> achieve that control. If this provides us with sufficient
> handles on human materials so that we can think of them as
> we think of metal parts, electrical power or chemical reactions
> then we have succeeded in placing human material on the same
> footing as any other material and can begin to proceed with
> our problems of systems design. '

He then goes on to describe in a quite depraved fashion the so-called disadvantages of using 'human operating-units',

> 'They're somewhat fragile. They're subject to fatigue,
> obsolescence, disease and even death. They're frequently
> stupid, unreliable and limited in memory capacity. But
> beyond all this they sometimes seek to design in their own
> cicuitry. This in a material is unforgivable. Any system
> utilising them must devise appropriate safeguards. '

In other words that which is most precious about human beings - their ability to 'design their own circuitry' (or think for themselves) is an attribute which should be suppressed by our design methodology. There are many equally graphic examples even in the field of intellectual work. I have an advert for computer aided design equipment and you don't have to be a sociological Einstein to understand what is meant by it. It says, 'If you've got a guy (it's always a 'guy' and never a woman, that actually designs - there are all the male chauvinist assumptions here) - If you've got a guy that can produce drawings non-stop all day, never gets tired or ill, never strikes, is happy on half pay and has got a photographic memory, then you don't need Uclid. ' The same sort of thing is being done to intellectual workers as has already happened on the workshop floor. Taylor once said 'In my system the work man is told precisely what he is to do and how he is to do it and any improvements he makes upon the instruction that is given to him are disastrous to success'. That is an assumption in design methodology which we should never accept. The most precious thing about human beings is that they think for themselves - to use their own imagination. Indeed it is this which separates human beings from primitive animal existence. A very long time ago Marx said,

> 'A bee puts to shame many an architect in the construction of
> its cells. But what distinguishes the worst of architects from
> the best of bees is mainly this: that the architect raises his
> structure in his imagination before he erects it in reality.
> At the end of every labour process we get a result that already
> existed in the imagination of the labourer at its beginning. '

In the Lucas Aerospace Corporate Plan the work force propose a range of equipment which will be socially useful and actually improve the quality of life rather than diminishing it. But we are also trying to devise a means of production in which human beings can once again give full vent to their creativity and where the skill and ability of our people (which is the greatest asset of our society) can be fully utilised in the interest of all. It is not machinery and technology that is our greatest asset. It is people. We are attempting to give back to people the right to use that ability.

TECHNOLOGY: THE LANGUAGE
OF SOCIAL ACTION
David Dickson

There has been growing criticism in recent years of the patterns of technological development adopted by both industrialised and underdeveloped countries. This is indeed implicit in the very title of this symposium; the need for a design for need, so to speak, already implies the existence, perhaps even the predominance, of a design that meets less desirable criteria. One can suggest private profit and political oppression.

But what is this need that design is supposed to meet? Although this question raises the basic issue to which my paper is addressed - namely the need for political, as well as technical action to ensure that technology meets true social needs - I do not want to answer it directly. Rather, I wish to concentrate on the type of answer that it is possible to give, and the type of technology that is subsequently developed to meet the need in question. I want to suggest that not merely the need itself, but equally the way that the need is determined, is reflected in the resulting technology, and that this technology can consequently be taken to articulate and express a society's mechanism for determining need, itself part of its dominant mode of social organisation and control - in other words, of its political structure

First, some attempts at definition. I suggest that we define, and think of, technology as an active social institution - rather like the law or education - where the mode of functioning is an implicit part of the definition.

A similar change in perspective is required in our definition of politics. Conventional interpretations often carry an arid abstractness with them. On the one hand, politics are used to refer to the administrative functions of the state, expressed in terms of the relative managerial abilities of rival political parties; who can manage inflation? or the unions? best, and so on. On the other, even within a socialist perspective, the word is often used to refer to large-scale and thus apparently abstract concepts such as class, capital, and so on.

Here again I want to suggest seeing the importance of political issues, not merely in terms of how the country - or the state - is run, but equally in the way that people relate to each other at a more personal level. For it is by grasping what has been called the 'politics of everyday life' that we can see how the abstract political forces described above are experienced by the individual in the very fabric of his or her existence, and in the case of a capitalist society, how the dominance of a capitalist class is experienced through treatment by employer, bank manager, even family and children.

I say this by way of introduction because I feel that it is important to talk about technology meeting social needs - i.e. technology meeting political objectives - not merely in terms of society-should-have-more-aids-for-the-disabled-and-less-colour-television-sets, important as this type of discussion is, but also in terms of society-should-have-the-means-of-generating-technological-forms-appropriate-to-the-needs-of-its-members. The distinction is perhaps slightly clearer if we turn the approach around, and express our criticism, not merely in terms of the uses to which technology is put, but equally in terms of the structural properties of the technology concerned. For example; rather than trying to attach the label good or bad to the motor car in abstract, the real need is to develop a framework within which we can criticise the type of way that the motor car is used, and then show how this is related to the form that the motor car takes.

Conventional interpretations of the concept of technology suggest that technology is essentially about doing things, about interactions between human beings and nature; the function of a technological process is to bring about some change in material conditions in accordance with some human purpose. I do not want to deny this inter-pretation, but there is another important way in which technology functions in society between individuals as a mode of communication. By this I mean that technology represents and transmits a particular way of dealing with the world, a particular set of 'material meanings'.

Perhaps this is clearer if I make a direct analogy with verbal speech. Speech is a mode of communication between individuals based on an agreed set of verbal meanings, expressed in what we call words. It can be said that these meanings constitute the way that we think of objects, phenomena and events. Now, just as verbal communication is an essential component of social life, so is material communication with the world of objects. I suggest that it is possible to make a direct analogy between verbal communi-cation (based on the use of words to express verbal meanings and ideas) and material communication (based on the use of tools and machines to express and transmit what I call material meanings) - ways not of thinking about the world but of dealing with it.

We can extend this to suggest a further analogy between the idea of a language (a com-bination of a society's words, its vocabulary, and the way that these are put together, its syntax) and the idea of a technology (a combination of a society's tools and machines and the way that these are put together). Hence, the title to this paper, 'Technology as a language of social action'.

This may sound very abstract, but before taking specific examples there is a further point to be made which is of central importance, namely recognition of the extent to which both the language of words and the language of machines serve political functions in society. There is not sufficient time available to go into the arguments in detail here, but merely to suggest that the ways of thinking about the world which are expressed through the use of words are, in fact, what are commonly referred to as 'ideologies', that is interpretations of events and phenomena that coincide with the political interests of a particular sector or class in society.

The same, I would now argue, can be said of technology. The way in which a society 'does things' is directly related to the way in which that society is organised and controlled. Think, for example, of the parallel rise of the factory system of production and industrial capitalism. A centralised hierarchical and authoritarian form of organisation and control over the production process represented by the factory matches the form of organisation and control within capitalism as a whole. The material meanings conveyed by technology are (like the verbal meanings of speech) not neutral. They tend, inevitably, to express the dominant ways of doing things within a society, and hence to reflect, reinforce and reproduce the dominant forms of social relationships on which these ways of doing things are based.

Here I would like to give three examples. The first is the case of the telephone. The technological characteristics of the telephone as a means of providing long-distance communication between individuals need little elaboration; neither does the central importance of the telephone in contemporary social life, where it has become an integral component of our complex network of social communication. Yet if we are to come to terms with the role of the telephone in society, we must ask not merely what it can do in theory, but what it does - and does not do - in practice. The conventional social critique of the telephone (or of the telephone system), concerns not the nature of the telephone apparatus, but the way that it is used. The technology is neutral; the social problems are associated essentially with its use. Here I am referring to the fact that the telephone is distributed through society on the basis of an ability to pay for the use of the service, and availability is therefore skewed in favour of those in possession of wealth, and hence in control of the means of production. I, as a journalist, can sit happily at my desk chatting to a contributor at the other end of Europe for fifteen minutes, while old people living on their own are unable to use the telephone for what is often a literally life-saving contact with the outside world.

This criticism is perfectly legitimate as far as it goes. There is a strong case indeed, for placing all important public services on the same basis as the National Health Service, equally available to all, regardless of ability to pay, and thus based on a system of need rather than wealth. At the same time, however, the use-abuse, 'technology is neutral' model is inadequate to answer certain structural criticisms of the telephone system. For, part of the reason the telephone system is as it is, is the fact that society is as it is. The desirable restructuring of the telephone system can only be properly achieved through the fundamental restructuring of society as a whole.

To be more explicit, Capitalist society is one in which social organisation and control is hierarchical and authoritarian in character; political power is concentrated in the hands of the few who possess wealth at the top, and imposed on the many who do not possess wealth at the bottom. As the 7:84 theatre group reminds us, seven per cent of the population own eighty-four per cent of the wealth, and I bet that they all own telephones. This form of organisation can be represented by the hierarchic tree, with an individual occupying each of the branch points.

Now the important point is that the channels of communication within the hierarchical tree are essentially one-to-one; each individual is in one-to-one contact with those immediately below him, who are in one-to-one contact with those below them, and so on (Think of the way that orders are 'passed down', for example, in the army.) And it is also the basic mode of operation of the telephone system which allows A to talk to B, B to talk to C, C to talk to D, and even, of course, A to talk to D. But what it does not allow is for all four individuals, A, B, C and D, to talk together. Or to be more precise, I should say that the telephone system as currently designed does not allow this type of conversation to take place as a matter of course. Technically it is, and has in fact always been, quite feasible. In the very early days of the telephone, before the days of radio a large number of listeners could dial into a sermon or a concert, a type of cable-radio. The Post Office still offer what it calls a Confravision service, whereby, with the appropriate payment a number of individuals can discuss a common topic simultaneously. But this is the exception, rather than the rule. And it is an exception which has nothing to do with technical considerations, but is because the dominant mode of communication within our modern capitalist society (and central to the functioning of that society) is based on one-to-one interactions.

The telephone system, I suggest, reinforces the patterns of dominance and control by facilitating one-to-one interactions which operates in favour of control from the top rather than the collectivist forms of interaction which operate in favour of control from below. Hence the telephone system is not neutral; the technology reinforces the forms of social organisation and control.

The second example I would like to consider is that of factory production, and in particular, the factory assembly line. Ever since Adam Smith the tendency in industrial production has been for each individual to carry out an increasingly small aspect of the overall production process. Of course, this is not necessarily a bad thing in itself; society could not exist without some form of division of labour. Yet an over-specialisation of labour, whatever its economic advantages to those in control, runs directly against the interests of the worker, who suffers not merely from the boredom and monotony of his work - a point explicitly recognised by those managers who hire the advice of 'job enrichment' experts - but from the increasing pressure that the division of labour enforces on him. Perhaps this is most clearly seen in the assembly line where the constant speed of the line places a continuous pressure on the workers to complete a certain task in a certain time. Individuals in the car industry, for example are selected for certain tasks - often those that are particularly well-paid - on the basis of their physical ability to work at speed, and are rapidly discarded as soon as the effects of working at such stress are removed. Similarly factory workers face various industrial hazards (from asbestosis to poly-vinyl-chloride) where it is the individual who is required to adapt to the demands of the machine - and hence to the economic demands of the machine owner - rather than the machine being adapted to meet the requirements, for safe working conditions.

Just as in the case of the telephone system, the technology of factory production is not neutral, but in its very form reflects and reinforces the political dominance of those who own the technology, rather than those who operate it. We can even see this in the lay-out of the factory floor, where the spatial separation of workers in, for example, a car factory limits social cohension within the works that might undermine the dominance of management. Things can be done differently, as the recent experiments in car factories in Sweden have demonstrated, where a number of individuals work jointly on a single car. It is no longer enough to say: there's nothing wrong with the technology, merely with the interests that it serves (or, in a more strictly Marxist terminology, 'there's nothing wrong with the means of production, merely with the form of the social relations of production'). What is now required is a more detailed understanding of the way in which the exploitative elements of a particular set of social relations are embedded in the very means of production -

whether in the assembly line or in the hazardous work situation - and indeed how these means of production express the dominant relations of production.

My final example is that of military technology. There is cause for increasing alarm in the new types of technology being introduced by Britain's military and police forces. Concern generated initially by the Campaign for Nuclear Disarmament and subsequently by campaigns against the Americans' use of chemical herbicides and defoliants in Vietnam, has since shifted nearer home to the vast new armoury of anti-personnel weapons being tested in Northern Ireland. These weapons range from incapacitating gases such as CS and CN, through the use of rubber bullets, to more sophisticated electronic devices whose exact nature only the army is aware of. Not only have many of these devices proved more damaging than was first thought - the number of deaths and injuries from the use of gas and rubber bullets is far from negligible - but equally important, they indicate a new style of military activity - counter-insurgency. I am concerned about the type of military technology which is now being developed with its emphasis on the need to control civilian populations and to keep a constant surveillance on the activities of political groups. Such forms of military technology again reflect and reinforce the class-basis of society. And it carries the specific danger, as in Northern Ireland, that attempts to impose a technological solution on political situations can exasperate rather than resolve the problems.

These three examples have I hope, indicated why I feel it is necessary to move forward from the criticism that modern technology is inherently oppressive (the Marcuse/Roszak argument so powerful a few years ago) or that technology is politically neutral. Our criticism should, I suggest, absorb not only the macro-technical issues, from Concorde to the atom bomb, but equally the technology of our everyday lives - systems of transport, of communication, of food production, even of cultural entertainment - from which the macro-issues seem deceptively remote. It is in this sense that I offer the concept of technology as a language of social action - a concept which allows us to see how technology articulates and expresses society's dominant patterns of organisation and control.

In a sense, this may appear very negative - merely theoretical waffle. 'Let's stop criticising and get down to doing things.' But it is just in getting down to doing things that I think part of the problem lies. It is all very well to design a new gadget, to discover a new source of energy, or indeed to develop a complete alternative technology. But society will only absorb a particular technology on any significant scale if the technology matches its priorities. New technologies will only have an effect if they can be developed together with new priorities. Where these priorities require structural changes in the way that society is organised (such as the re-distribution of wealth according to need, the establishment of collective decision making and collective responsibility, and so on) then, any attempts to achieve this situation merely through technological means are only technocratic utopianism. If we want a society that genuinely designs for need, then we must create a society which is prepared to recognise and cater for that need. We have a responsibility to demand such a society, and if necessary, to fight for it.

REFERENCES

T Roszak, The Making of a Counter Culture (London, Faber 1970)

E F Schumacher, Small is Beautiful (London, Blond and Briggs 1973)

P Harper & G Boyle (Ed), Radical Technology (London, Wildwood House 1976)

D Dickson, Alternative Technology and the Politics of Technical Change (London, Fontana 1974)

B Brown, Marx, Freud and the Critique of Everyday Life (Monthly Review Press, New York 1973)

J R Carroll (Ed), Language, Thought and Reality; Selected Writings of Benjamin Lee Whorf (New York 1976)

C Clutterbuck, Death in the Plastics Factory (Radical Science Journal, No 4 1976)

The New Technology of Repression (British Society for Social Responsibility in Science)

CONCEPTUAL DESIGN - A POLEMIC
Brian Smith

The conference title, 'Design for Need', supposes that design is not at the moment
for need, or for the right needs, and that we ought to change things. However, an
advertisement for the conference in the American Industrial Design Magazine
makes no reference whatsoever to the meaning of the conference title. Instead, above
a picture of a British Airways 747, the words calculated to grab the minds of the
industrial designers reading them are as follows: 'All inclusive tax-deductible
professional events ... plus a super vacation in London at a remarkably low budget
cost. Only $666 from New York. '

Further, the title is, as often, ambiguous. A recent conference at Portsmouth was
called 'Changing Design'. That too was perfectly chosen. We get into our planes
and boats and trains full of enthusiasm - 'I'm going to Change Design'; 'I'm going to
Design for peoples' Needs. ' And on the way back, when boredom has set in, when the
weight of papers has pressed us firmly back into our comfy chairs, we see that really
we went as voyeurs. The meaning of the words changed, the cube flipped, and we
listened to people talking about how design was changing, and how design is for peoples
needs, which we already knew, but fooled ourselves that we had not come to be told
yet again.

I suggest that notwithstanding the few good things that do emerge from such conferences, our pretensions for them are bullshit. We know this, and appear to care
very little.

We do not need to be told that the world has problems. But what is to be done about
them? As with an illness, surely we want to both eliminate the cause and alleviate
the symptoms? Both must be undertaken, with the first aid being directed towards
the immediate problems. You might think this is obvious - on seeing someone lying
bleeding in the road, we do not immediately run to petition the local council for a
pedestrian crossing; rather, we try to stop the bleeding. (There is, of course, a
school of thought which says that we should do nothing. As more and more people
die on this road, the council will be forced to ban traffic from it, saving more lives
in the long run. Similarly, the 'don't knows' should be tempted across the road by
some means, when they will hopefully end up bruised or frightened enough to join the
storm on the council - 'There is nothing so radicalising as a blow from a policeman's
fist'.) But what does the designer do in this road accident situation?

Typically, sits down to design the form that the petition to the council might take. Or
pursues a two-year research programme on the analysis of pedestrian movement near
road junctions. If he or she has a leaning towards Alternative Technology, the design
might be for a new sort of tourniquet made out of Kleenex tissues and lollipop sticks,
and making sure everyone knows how to use it. All these stances are justifiable by

someone - they must be, since no-one does what they consider to be unjustifiable, and people certainly do things analogous to these.

We reply; 'It's not as simple as that', to someone who suggests that longterm elasto-plast research is all very well but what about the causes of today's casualties, 'It's not as simple as that'. Of course society ought to be changed so that everyone has somewhere good to live, but it's not as simple as that. Of course my designs for educational equipment and medical tools would be better if the government thought them one hundredth as important as nuclear weapons, but ... it's not as simple as that.

Perhaps someone can explain the difference between the attitude of one who says to a homeless person 'it's not as simple as that', and the 'callous revolutionary attitude' (naturally deplored by all) that says people should be left to die or to be oppressed: because only when they're at breaking point will they rise up to change things. What is the difference? What are we to say to people, on the one hand sacrificed to political expediency, on the other to our apparent inability to extract a simple major problem from a mass of minor ones? 'Half the world's starving' say the headlines; and in the stop press ... 'Designer comes up with new sort of toothbrush.'

So what happens to our ideals? How do design students with radical ideas seem to end up a few years later designing hotel interiors, lighting, chairs and so on? I suggest that they fall into the Reformist Trap. They find that if they don't suppress their beliefs to some extent, then they can't cope with what they need to do to 'make a living'. The best they can do is to try and change things within their own particular sphere of influence, harming others as little as possible, in the hope that they can help to alter things bit by bit.

The objections to this approach are as follows:

> We make our sphere of influence so small. We'd feed a starving man in our house, but probably not if he was in the next street, let alone another country.

> Harming 'as little as possible' is very situation-specific, yet we generalise it for ourselves, and accept others' rational-isations willingly.

> Do we really hope for the big changes? If tomorrow is too soon, but the year 2000 too late for a revolution, just when is a revolution 'acceptable'?

> We go berserk with rage when six people die in a bombing, yet refuse to give any meaningful amounts of money to charities helping thousands that are dying now of war, disease, famine - people we could do something about. So we have: 'hanging is too good for those terrorists', and 'I don't give very much to charities - they spend too much on administration'.

Thomas Markus' paper at the 1971 Design Participation conference (1) is the most accurate analysis of the differences between reformist and revolutionary designers that I have seen. The former, typically from a middle-class leftish background, try to make the design process transparent to the public gaze, and to provide ranges of alternative solutions so that compromises may be effected. But the revolutionary rejects both this and the conservative/patronage-oriented way, in favour of working for a real transfer of power. His clients are the end users and his work is often voluntary. He is not afraid of value judgements and he often rejects 'participation', not least for its potential for political manipulation.

Well, five years later, we begin to see the glimmerings of a recognition of this revolutionary role. The most recent New Scientist (2) carries an article headlined 'Windmill builders become political', reflecting changes in both the environmentalist and radical technology movements towards a disbelief that 'an accumulation of small changes will, by itself, lead to overall social and political changes'. Of course we all know this is true. That's the trouble with designers. You can call for Cultural Revolution Tomorrow ... or Yesterday ... and you're preaching to the converted. It's just that it never happens. Who do you want to hear ... Schumacher? 'Don't try to out-capitalise the capitalists'; and he quotes the capitalists' hallucinatory cry 'We are all socialists now' ... Illich? 'Only a cultural and institutional revolution which re-establishes man's control over his environment can arrest the violence by which development of institutions is now imposed by a few for their own interest '(3) ... Papanek? 'Design must be revolutionary and radical ...'(4)

You may say that I want to change design by or into politics. But I don't. I argue for the opposite case, of design changing society and politics, not merely seeking to diminish a misfit between existing situations.

However, there is no avoiding the fact that design as decision-making becomes political as soon as more than one person is involved. One striking example from my own experience (6) is that of a Danish charity who used a computer model to respond much more effectively with emergency disaster relief. But many of the limitations and parameters that the system could apply were political in origin - nakedly political - such as country X only giving certain supplies if they were transported by a particular airline and if certain other, completely useless supplies were bought - and only then so long as country Y's aid was not accepted until later.

But how can design change politics? Answer: we are in the unique position of dealing with potentially completely general problems - the design of everything, and not just tangible things, either. We are luckier even than the systems thinkers, the Cybernauts who can only say what is and hope to point the way forward or to base successive operations on the new theories that emerge as they creep slowly forward along the hypothetico-deductive spiral. Designers are better off. By all means let us use the fashionable scientific paradigm - it works for biological warfare, and it can work for us. But we are supposed to be artistically creative too - we can damn-well invent our own paradigms, right out of the blue, just like that and design our dreams into reality and no-one will be very surprised.

Design's practitioners can operate inside a giant and immediate feedback system in which hypothesis and deduction, simulation, action, thought, intuition, logic, art, polemics, creativity, objectivity and subjectivity can all thrive. Yet what does design have to say to society today? It has to say - and I paraphrase a recent metaphor by a professor of design research - that we are sailing around on a stormy sea with no particular place to go, so we'll try to design better aids to navigation, better bilge pumps, stronger sails. Design does not teach us how to swim - still less how to stop that bloody wind blowing.

Today's 'radical design' tells us to participate. 'User participation', said Nigel Cross in his preface to the Design Participation proceedings, 'by involving in the design process those who will be affected by its outcome, may provide a means for eliminating potential problems at their source'. Too right. One of the chief potential problems being that of protest and action after the event. With the magic ingredient of 'participation', all the people with the power have to do is to turn round and say 'How can you moan about this building (or whatever) - you participated in its design.' Most 'participation' is on the level of one's jailers asking if one prefers the rope or the firing squad. Many people instinctively know this, which allows the authorities to throw up their hands and say 'You see - even when we offer you a say, you don't want it'.

I cannot emphasise strongly enough how harmful I believe the notion of 'participation' to be. It is a spectacle to distract us, a sop to the masses, a manoeuvre carried out largely by hypocrites with bad intentions. No government dares carry participation to its logical conclusions ... and in practice they do not need to worry, because it is self-regulating: by definition diminishing its own energy as peoples' needs appear to get answered. When people talk about 'participation', I believe they mean 'limited participation', 'reasonable participation'. I for one do not wish to confront some of the grosser results of the world's tragedies with talk of limits and reasonableness.

So far, so destructive ...

If conferences are a con, reform is retrograde and participation placatory, what should designers do? Simple. Apart from a few special cases, they should stop designing - at least under the present terms of reference. To the people designing doorknobs, cars, hairdriers, radios, packages, chairs, beds, and tractors and bandages, we should say 'STOP - THE ONES WE'VE GOT WILL DO'. You've been so clever, such good designers, that nearly everything we make and use is just about good enough now, considering all these other problems we've got.'

Design as we know it should be replaced by what I have called Conceptual Design, so-called because I want it to relate to the true meaning of design, which is by no means necessarily object-oriented; and also by analogy with Conceptual Art.

As to the meaning of the word 'design', we can all play around with definitions, but if we refer to the Thesaurus, which lists words according to meanings, we can trace links and connections between two or more words. For example, 'design' and 'revolution' coincide at 'change', while 'design' and 'politics' give 'plan'. However, 'design', 'existence' and 'truth' give a bi-pole, involving both 'creation, uniqueness, transcendence' and 'unity, equality, oneness, not distinguish'. It is this polarisation that I want to pursue, and which is embodied in the idea of Conceptual Design.

The relation to Conceptual Art is simple: however much that art has been incorporated into the very structures it sought to make irrelevant, it started off with a total rejection of the bourgeois notions of what art previously was. It is surprising to realise that only in the last ten or fifteen years have we come to see words as art, earthworks as art, documentation, events and happenings as art. To quote Joseph Kosuth (7) on Conceptual Art, but substituting design words for his art words, 'Being a designer now means to question the nature of design. But if one is questioning the nature of house design, one cannot be questioning the nature of design ... if you design houses, toothbrushes or consoles, you are already accepting, not questioning, the nature of design.'

Again: obviously, naturally, of course ... we claim to know this already. Let us then go on to criticise the almost total dedication of the concerned group of designers (which I take the people at Design for Need to be) to Third World, low technology or handicap-remedial situations. This group is already only a small fraction of all designers. Of the rest, that percentage who fail to respond to the call to stop 'designing' should be ignored. They are probably in it for the money, and might as well be selling second-hand cars. In an ideal world we would educate people and seek to change attitudes gradually ... but there is not time. So forget the rest. However, if only one in ten of those who say 'I'd do something if I could' really mean it, then we're OK. They should initially 1) make propaganda to increase awareness, 2) act, and 3) simulate and theorise. In doing 2) and 3) successfully, they would be doing 1) anyway.

Conceptual Design says designers should polarise, basically into theorists and activists, according to skill and inclination. Apart from an effort - and an increase in today's terms - to make at least tolerable the lives of those who are worst off, everyone else presently concerned with design, with their skills in implementing and reading structures, organisations, in practical problem solving, in decision-making, should do one of two things: First, get out on the streets, act, change, fight, recognise that we do not have time to do anything slowly, 'carefully', 'reasonably'; that these words, in the mouths of those who most often counsel their value, frequently do not mean what the dictionary says they mean. They are more laden with value-judgement than anything I say here.

Or second, they should be designing concepts, and incorporating them into systems that will enable the most effective implementation of solutions to problems, in ways that are completely open to people for their own use in solving other problems. In short, the theorists for the cultural revolution.

To reiterate, the two parts of this totally connected couple consist in recognising that we must go out and change things with what we've got, without waiting for better tools for the job; and in the radical re-appraisal of all that design might be. The relation between this idea and Papanek's 'Integrated Design' is one of a possibly reckless urgency applied to that concept, in the belief that morally, logically, and with regard to time, we have no choice.

Conceptual Design will enable us to act on the truths we already know, but are so brilliant at avoiding. If you want a conference, let's have it in Bangladesh or Guatemala, or North Kensington ... anywhere but here. And if the selfish natives have not seen fit to build a conference centre, let one of the first Conceptual Design projects be how to encourage both theorists and activists to work constantly rubbing shoulders with the problems they're dealing with. Which of us could stand surrounded by starving, homeless people and say ... 'Hang on chaps, only 137 more to die, and then I'll have your plans drawn up.' People constantly say (and this is the last line of defence) 'but we'd all go mad if we were really aware of all the suffering'. Conceptual Design must take us as far in that direction as we can bear to go.

So Conceptual Designers will produce devices, tangible or not, that will bring other peoples' problems within our range, demonstrating that physical and social distances are not the criteria to apply to decisions on aid and action.

They will also offer procedures rather than designed objects per se, so that what people do with or within them is a product of their own experience, circumstances and needs. They should be rich in analogy, so we can generate our own procedures and hence the objects, events, systems, organisations and structures that we need.

Thirdly, we will be made aware of a wholeness that we seem to have lost, and of the fact that whatever part of humanity is lost before we get round to designing our way out of it, then it is part of ourselves that we have murdered, by default.

We must persuade people away from design as it is now and, still leaving many more people than at present helping those whose lives are intolerable, work out a simple problem, each of us for ourselves. The question is, if present rates of death and horror are unacceptable, do we adopt a possibly risky revolutionary course that might work, or do we pursue the present reformist policy that most of us know in our hearts, never will? For there is not time. Ask anyone who's dying.

REFERENCES

1) T Markus, Design Participation (N Cross, Ed) Academy Press, London, 1972)

2) J Hanlon, Windmill builders become political (New Scientist, 8 April 1976

3) I Illich, Celebration of Awareness (Penguin Education, London, 1973) pp 147-156

4) V Papanek, Design for the Real World (Paladin, 1974)

5) R Guite, Impressions of the 'Design Activity' Conference (DMG-DRS J 1973 Vol 7, No 4) p 280

6) B R Smith, Can computers cut the waste in disaster relief? (New Scientist, Oct 1974) p 335

7) J Kosuth, Idea Art (G Battcock, Ed) (Dutton, New York, 1973)

PERSON TO PERSON DESIGN
Oliver Hawkins

Over the years the idea that serious industrial design must be on a large scale has become almost a cornerstone of establishment thinking. The arguments are convincing enough: scale allows time for substantial research and development (and therefore better designs), it allows economies of production (and therefore lower prices) and of course it gets to more people. It also has the attraction of longer term, more secure financing, and the very real appeal of appearing somehow truly professional, to a desperately insecure profession.

In addition to this there exists among many designers a suspicion of small scale design, for individual clients, as being necessarily expensive and elitist: Hicks interiors, Makepeace furniture, Zandra Rhodes dresses; designs that, however beautiful they may be, seem not to answer the real questions.

So this has led to the widespread belief that design cannot be satisfactory without massive research, and that prices cannot be reasonable outside mass production. The consumer appears to be left with the choice, as it were, of Harley Street or Roche pharmaceuticals.

And, logically enough, conscientious designers want to apply the same 'serious' scale to projects for real need. After all, if that much time and trouble is spent developing a washing-up machine, surely at least as much should go towards something more critically needed.

But in a number of areas large scale design is inoperative or inadequate. These tend in the nature of things to be minority areas, such as items for the disabled. In these areas a small scale effort, sometimes ridiculously small, can pay off. This has been brought home to me very clearly in my college's dealings with local hospitals and institutions. Having gone in thinking we might be able to offer odd murals and mobiles and toys, we've been surprised to be asked for all kinds of items of equipment, some of them absolutely basic. And I've been rather appalled to find that items designed and made by my young and inexperienced students have been preferred to some of those sent through from the purchasing office. Why sholud this be? Over the course of two dozen or so projects I have attempted to analyse the advantages. Where are the openings for person-to-person design?

Firstly, very simply, where there is nothing else available. A typical case of this sort was when we were asked to find a way of getting a little boy with no legs down a steep shingle beach to the sea to bathe. Because the problem was unique there was no chance of ringing up Harrods and saying 'What have you got for getting legless children down pebbley beaches?' and in any case there was very little money. In the event what the student came up with was a track, made up of the thick rubber blankets

114

used by litho printers. These could be got for nothing once used, and were roped
together to form a smooth, movable pathway for the child or his bearer.

The second opening is where there is an existing solution, but inadequately distributed.
One of the students, George, used to work nights as an auxilliary nurse in a big
hospital, and he spent his time going round with pieces of wire and lengths of string,
rigging up all sorts of contraptions for the patients; on wheelchairs, on beds, all over
the place. One thing he did was to wrap foam rubber round the handles of cutlery,
for patients with arthritis and impaired grip. Now we all know that cutlery exists,
designed precisely for this purpose, and much better than what George rigged up. But
it hadn't reached this big, rich hospital, so the choice was between George's or
custard down the pyjamas.

The third opportunity for small scale work is where there is an existing solution, but
not good enough. One of the fundamental weaknesses of the mass production system
must be that one design has to suit a lot of different people. Usually it does, but
sometimes it clearly cannot. It is extraordinary how often one is asked to design a
special chair for someone, because nothing available seems right. We are working
at present on a commode, an unglamorous but necessary item for some handicapped
children, because the hospital is exasperated with standard ones. Even if one per-
cent of mass produced items are unsatisfactory, that still means an enormous field
of opportunity. If those are the opportunities, what are the advantages that make them
worth taking?

First of all, individual solutions. Sometimes a totally new concept, usually much less;
perhaps a couple of inches changed here and there, an extra piece, a new colour.
The individuality is not limited to considerations of function. Designing for someone
whose face you know demands and allows a much greater commitment to aesthetic
adventure.

Interestingly, it often turns out that something designed for one person is eventually
used by dozens; and yet I doubt whether as satisfactory a solution would have emerged
if that had been the initial intention. It is a process of working towards general
applications from below rather than above.

The second advantage is that of immediacy; the fact that a few minutes with your
individual consumer is worth a whole telephone directory of paper research. And the
fact that a solution may be available in a few days or even hours. When we were
working with thalidomide children we were very conscious that there was only one
age group involved, and that delay would invalidate the entire effort. This is of
course unusual, but the short term is a high price to pay for the chance of better
things another day.

The immediacy also helps mitigate the problem of cost of individual treatment. If a
solution can be found in the time it would normally take to identify the parameters of
the initial research programme, then clearly person-to-person design is in business.
But the savings also come in the elimination of large scale production development and
tooling costs, and the increasing expenses of distribution and promotion.

At a rather more general level the individual design process helps the consumer to understand that designers do not dispense magic, that designs are not sacred objects, but things that can be altered and adapted, repaired and re-cycled; perhaps even designed by the consumer himself next time round. We are often asked to do things that the consumer could perfectly well do himself. I liked the attitude of a hospital director, who, when an outsize patient broke a chair we had made, took it home and brazed on a great lump of angle iron to hold it together. And let's remember Alastair Best's slogan: 'You can have any colour as long as it is undercoat'.

These then are some of the advantages, but they are, I believe, secondary to the greatest value of person-to-person design: that of helping the designer himself to understand his role; helping him to grasp that design should be a service rendered rather than a package delivered.

'Design is about people' we say. We say it all the time, but what are people? Those dimensioned outlines on pale blue paper? Those convenient groups like C2D and AB? (and E that we never seem to come across).

I sometimes think designers resent real people. They're odd and inconvenient, they have strange habits and come in silly sizes, and there is something embarrassingly personal about them. It took an ad man rather than a designer to say 'Don't talk down to the consumer, she's your wife', and although that may have a sexist ring today the point remains.

Industrial designers find themselves in a delicate position, poised somewhere between the extremes of aesthetics and calculation. This position should give them their strength, but sadly, they often seem like slow children in a game of musical chairs, left standing and out of the game, or panicking and jumping on to the knee of some quicker child who's already found a seat. Thus, no sooner have designers got over feeling bad at not being artists, than they indulge in the equally fatuous regret at not being engineers. But if they are designers they cannot cling to either extreme; they must communicate delight as well as solving problems, solve problems as well as communicating delight.

And whereas the artist or the engineer can pursue his subject on its own terms, even for its own sake, the designer is only valid in terms of a third party, the user. If design is about people it cuts both ways; without users there is no such thing as design.

This, fundamentally, is why it is such a positive experience to work on a person-to-person basis; why George with his bits of wire and string has in some ways a truer understanding of design than some other student producing elegant magic-marker schemes for a Twenty-first Century Third World city car.

Sir Misha Black made a point about craftsmanship a few years ago: 'A period of handiwork is, I believe, essential to the development of all designers, even if they are destined to work eventually in the more cerebral design disciplines'. I suggest that in a similar way person-to-person experience is an essential part of the designer's comprehension of his role. I'm not suggesting that this scale of work should make up more than a tiny fraction of the total, any more than Sir Misha intended design studios to fill up with chisels and cherry wood every time a new job came in.

You may already be categorising what I have spoken about as alternative design. I hope not. The word alternative has picked up a smugness that invites you to take sides, writing off one or the other: mercenary purveyors of wasteful consumer durables versus hippies making shacks out of old beer cans and bits of other peoples' cars.

The last thing we need to do is to take sides. Design must by its nature operate at every possible level and scale, depending on the various and varying circumstances and requirements. No design is alternative, or, if you prefer, all of it is. As far as the ideals are concerned I would be more than happy if we were to reach a stage where the idea of person-to-person design no longer implied small scale, and where the title 'Design for Need' no longer implied guilt.

Design for Need? But of course.

TWELVE METHODOLOGIES FOR DESIGN - BECAUSE PEOPLE COUNT
*Prof. Victor **Papanek***

Professor Papanek's presentation was given extempore. The text which follows has been produced from a tape taken at the time. It is heavily reduced from its original bulk for the present purpose.

I would like to illustrate my twelve strategies with a large number of slides, all of which without exception, show work by former students of mine, largely in Great Britain and in Denmark. But before I begin I'd like to bring to your attention three statements which will save you the problem and the expense of buying 'Design for the Real World'.

Design should be a prosperous and multidisciplinary team activity that includes workers and users.

Design must be concerned with the social, political, ecological, environmental, ecological stability and resource consequences of design intervention.

Design should neither be elitist nor untherapeutic as far as the designers are concerned, since most designers do tend to design for themselves.

Now, I would like to begin with a cluster of questions, some of which have been raised by this conference. For instance we have been told a great deal about the social forces that influence design or should influence or might or could. My faith in social influences on design is not very strong. I hasten to add that my faith in the influence of design on social forces doesn't exist at all. But comparing industrial design activities in various parts of the world then, it seems that results are rather similar, if one were to compare the political and social systems of Britain or the United States or West Germany of Japan or what have you. So suppose you then take those countries which are generally called Socialist - Imperialist, like the Soviet Union and some of the countries in Eastern Europe, and say that that's a second 'camp' of countries; and if you were then to assume that the Peoples Republic of China is radically different in outlook then that is a third kind of country; and if you were then to assume that the so-called peripheral, Third World countries were a sort of fourth 'camp'; and if you were then to say that drop-out hippy communes in places like Sweden and the United States are a fifth 'camp' - then how do they all relate themselves to design?

Well the Soviet Union, three months ago, hired the most established and elderly firm of industrial designers in the United States. The Peoples Republic of China has ten days ago retained two large industrial design groups, one from Japan and one from the United States. A great deal of design for so-called Third World countries is being done by happy volunteers from countries like Sweden, Denmark, Finland, Norway and West and East Germany. A lot of the institutional work is being handled by West German, Japanese and American design firms. And I was startled and interested to find out that those things which drop-out, 'hippie' communes make for export (in for instance the United States) are usually designed for them by designers who've been through a regular industrial design trade. So I have, as I've said, little faith in social forces shaping design. I think it's a 'herring', red or otherwise, that's not all that important.

So what is 'alternative design' now? I know what alternative design was ten years ago because ten years ago a lot of people, myself included, proposed design for developing countries and design for elderly people and design for handicapped people, etc. Well, the trouble is that the ideas have won through - and certainly Denmark concerns itself a great deal now, as does Finland, with design for 'normal' and handicapped children, and Sweden has addressed itself to the question of the elderly and a number of countries are interested in giving help to peripheral countries. So what really is 'alternative design' these days? And for that matter, why do so many people work with developing countries and the elderly and the handicapped? One of the theories that I'm slowly beginning to develop is that it's because they tend to be rather helpless groups and its easier to experiment on the handicapped, the elderly, small children and peripheral countries than it is to experiment upon say, the economic policy of the Federal German Republic or the United States or Japan. I think there is a degree of victimisation and exploitation involved in all of this.

Just in parenthesis, it is interesting to find out, for those of us who do want to help the peripheral countries ... that if you travel in Africa for instance you'll see hundreds of volunteers (again largely from Denmark, Sweden, Norway and Finland) in Kenya - but not in the Sudan. Now the reason is that the climate in Kenya is delightful and the climate in the Sudan is bad. It's obviously easier to get people to help in Kenya, but not the Sudan because it's rather hot and dusty and, while there is a genuine desire to help peripheral countries, it might be pleasanter to do it in comparative comfort.

Now one of the things that I've become very interested in over the last two years is the alienation between people and designed products. The people in this case could be either the user of designed products or the makers of designed products - alienation exists in both cases. I was introduced to this when working for Volvo of Sweden and dealing with 'work-enrichment programmes' for their workers. I realised that the majority of the workers at Volvo really dislike working on Volvo automobiles. Now I think the important thing is that it's an overall problem. The people of the Peoples Republic of China find some of the cameras made by Seagull, (the largest Chinese camera firm) equally alienating - from the package right through to the camera itself. Certainly work-alienation has grown in China among the assembly line workers - not to the extent of Sweden or the United States, but it's there. And so I suggest that some of the problems in design transcend the questions of peripheral vis-à-vis metropolitan areas. They transcend the problems of different political systems such as Capitalist, Socialist - Imperialist, mixed economy, Communist, Socialist, 'drop-out' communes, flipped-out-people and so forth because they're really sort of 'people-problems'.

But there are some ways of dealing with the various constituencies that designers theoretically serve. I've written down here twelve ways - these of course are just words - and in terms of slides all I can show you are some very tentative experiments that students of mine and I have made.

So let's go back to square one. There seems to be general agreement that the main
problem of design lies in the interface between design and people. That's where the
problem is; and that's where the interface is; and that's where the action is. And if tha
is true, then what do we do about it? My answer is 'I don't know - but I have one or two
suggestions'.

RECONNECT

To illustrate this I'm using slides on work that was done by a student of mine at
Manchester Polytechnic, a year ago. In the UK polo hats come in eight sizes, riding
helmets come in four sizes, and working helmets come in one size. There are in
Europe something like 180 different types of skiing goggles and only three types of
protective glasses for people at work. I am not suggesting that the pious intentions of
the designer (whether we use the word correctly or not) are going to change this. Whe
I say 'reconnect' I'm suggesting that industrial design, rather than working for industr
should work for the Trade Unions. That is one of the reconnections that can be made
in fact two of my students are investigating working directly for the TUC.

The sheltering of ears from loud work processes tends to be something that isolates
workers very much. (By the way, if any of you have the choice of going blind or going
deaf, please choose blindness - for in my understanding deafness is much more
difficult to handle psychologically.) If you put ear muffs on people, in actual practice
you make them deaf. Now obviously it is the job of industry to sound-proof work
processes to the extent of giving protection of our hearing. Another thing about ear

protectors is that if someone needs to give you a message such as 'Look Out!' the man to receive can't hear it. The student Roger Dalton designed ear communicators that conduct micro-pulses, so that in-line communication is possible.

Getting round to the problem of welding hats, he began developing better ones - lighter weight ones with photo-tropic plastic scatters. Please remember that I am not showing these things as good or bad student design - I'm suggesting these as one direction of reconnection between the designer and the Trade Unions.

BROADEN

This is a scales designed for Habitat of Britain who were unhappy over the fact that kitchen weighing machines are largely imported from Italy, Denmark and Germany rather than British built. This one is designed by a student at Manchester Polytechnic, to be of service to blind people, sighted people and people with minimal eyesight. There is a 'broadening' of the constituencies, with a concern for a broad group, and a second 'broadening' in that it is specifically designed to be built by blind people.

And this last year in Canada a class under Professor Michael Kammelmeyer, working on similar projects, began a scale for the blind and badly-sighted to be built at Shelter Workshops. This is an electronic scales that, with a series of three buzzes, tells you when you are overweight, underweight, or just right.

Jim Hennessy provisionally designed this Braille writer for blind people - this is just a working model. What is significant about it is that, while it is made for blind people to make notes in Braille, it is built by the mentally retarded - again there is a broadening of the constituencies.

REDEFINE

There is the peculiar fact that there are a number of things we buy or own for absolutely no good reason - for instance vacuum cleaners. In the area in which I now live in Ottawa there is a total of twenty-four houses with twenty-four families owning something like thirty vacuum cleaners and twenty-two lawn mowers. Now the objection to sharing vacuum cleaners is a very simple one. If you lend your vacuum cleaner to somebody, he'll bring it back broken, because vacuum cleaners haven't been designed for sharing. So in redefining for this kind of constituency, this student of mine in Manchester designed a vacuum cleaner specifically for sharing and hopes to extend this to various other tools.

What's the difference between a shared and a non-shared tool? Well the problem is cheap changeability of parts, easy understanding and so forth. I think that bicycle technology is the perfect example of an open-ended tool that lends itself to sharing. The Bickerton Bike, which we have worked on the last year and a half, has been I think a breakthrough in bicycle technology in that it is the only folding bike that weighs 3 lbs less than an Italian racing bike, which weighs somewhere near about 72 lbs. But I shan't weary you with the design development of that.

This is a vehicle for harvesting the coffee crop. It will carry, with one man pedalling, his weight and 600 lbs; with two men pedalling it will carry the weight of the two people

and around 850 lbs. It will go over uneven terrain, and the idea behind it was to keep
pollution out of the coffee plantation. The vehicle is not made in a factory (which is
to me the relevant aspect about it). It's made in little bicycle shops all over Guatemal
and Cuba, and each shop can customise the vehicle (if that's the right word) for the
local conditions which are less or more hilly. It is, as you can see, a canabalised
vehicle made out of used parts - used truck parts, used bicycle parts, transmissions,
and what have you. About 6, 000 vehicles have been built in Guatemala, and I am told
that a similar number have been made in Cuba.

SIMPLIFY

On the right hand are some pumps. We felt quite strongly (we, in this case, being
UNESCO) that Chad was a good place for using this type of pump. The difficulty here
was that the Chadiennes do not take kindly to innovation of any sort. So a simple
strategy had to be worked out. The way Oxfam developed it for us was this: they had
a man open a small shop in the market place, where he had a big sign saying 'We buy
old tyres : two shillings for a tyre'. People would find old tyres and bring them in and
they'd get two shillings. Then a week later he had another sign up saying 'I sell
pumps : eighty shillings per pump'. Then people got very angry because they felt
'why we can do that ourselves'. This is how technology is transferred.

If you break your arm or your leg, when the plaster is removed it tends to be done with
a surgical instrument known as a Black and Decker saw. The difficulty is that it leaves
a thin red line up your arm or leg or whatever. So one of the post-graduate students
at Manchester worked on this rechargeable saw. The blade runs between a couple of
nylon wheels and nibbles off the plaster just as fast as you can go.

HUMANISE

Going one step further towards humanisation - the government of Nigeria (I should
probably say the government of Nigeria two and a half governments ago) - last year the
government of Nigeria found itself in the difficulty of having 238 tribal languages and
dialects with a largely illiterate population who tend to get much of their instruction by
the oral tradition. It was decided that the software of the system that deals with birth
control, agricultural education and various other pieces of information would be taped
on tape cassettes in the various different languages and then Nigeria would build its
own tape cassette players. We took about fifty or so tape cassette players from
Phillips into the bush. (I should explain that is not an attempt to use third-rate
technology in the Third World. In places like Nigeria, tape recorders and cassette
players exist and people use them in the cities - in the bush they do not.)

So we brought about fifty tape cassette recorders into the bush and gave them to
people to see if there were any difficulties - if they had trouble learning with them.
And we felt that the only trouble had to do with the alignment of the batteries. It was
difficult to deal with a pre-literate population and teach them the difference between a
plus sign and a minus. This just happened to be one of the difficulties.

So we designed this and its being made in Nigeria. It's an injection moulded plastic
case. (The case is there because there is vermin in many developing countries that
is attracted by the insulation wiring round the electronic parts.) So it's very simple

and it's also exported by Nigeria to other West and East African countries who have money.

But that leaves West and East African countries and Asian countries that do not have money. And what happens here is that they can buy, at much lower cost, this gadget in a little plastic bag and then be given comic books on how to build alternative coverings, on a cottage or village level - some using a wooden technology, some using a flattened-tin-can technology, some using a thin line ceramic technology and some using a technology of calabash and bamboo. We have a sixty page comic book for each of these technologies, all of them non-verbal.

DEMONSTRATE

This is a lamp specifically designed by a student from Denmark for Indonesian needs. In Indonesia the majority of people are afraid of the dark and there's a shortage of electricity. There's also the universal need in peripheral countries, not only to have a better foreign exchange situation, but to raise the degree of national pride among the people. So this is exported now all over South Asia, under the name 'the Java Lamp'. The upper part is made of a fishing float which is already made in Badung in normal production. It has a dimmer switch that conserves electricity (unlike most dimmer switches when the light is dim). The clips come off in the morning and the dead insects drop out. The clips and the other metal items are made on the Isle of Bali by the village grouping that normally makes metal bound boxes.

These are two demonstrable things - the one on the right is highly demonstrable. It's an electronic metronome designed by Michael Morris, a student at Manchester, which makes it possible for people with severe stuttering problems to talk quite normally (although in a mono-tone) after somewhere between three or five minutes of practice.

The one on the left was concerned with the problem that not only do children die in bathroom accidents in this country but in addition to that retarded children have problems being bathed. So this bath restrainer was designed for Mothercare.

DECENTRALISE

Now this is highly theoretical and I shall only tell you about it because it's a sort of hobby-horse of mine. In Britain we were able to locate 5,000 areas in which one could use a vehicle that was not quite an ambulance or a fire engine, but was more than just a car. And we then began investigating the basic vehicles that are really cheap, like the Volkswagen Golf or the Moskowitch, the Seagull (again from China), the Citroen 2 - CV, the Renault 5, the Fiat 126 and in this country, the BMC Mini Van. We began designing a series of re-conversions. Assuming that there might be seven or eight crofter cottages somewhere, or a Solente Club, or people on an island, who already owned a mini van, they could not only convert it into an emergency vehicle (and in that way decentralise medical and fire services to some degree) but also 'customise' the vehicle to the specific needs of the community. The work on this is still being carried on by six other students.

ENABLE

Here we have an experiment, again in Manchester. Market gardeners (people who grow mushrooms, blueberries, strawberries etc) had written wanting to make various baskets, from time to time, of different shapes and sizes. Probably the most useful tool they could have is a small vacuum-former but rather than building vacuum-formers we did a comic book showing how to build your own. Then there is a secondary comic book showing you how to vacuum-form now that you've got the vacuum-former.

But we then began to get into the next participatory and enabling area. What would happen if things came more as do-it-yourself kits?

Some of the most difficult things in the world only come in do-it-yourself kits. For instance there's absolutely no way to buy an inexpensive harpsichord - you have to build it yourself from a kit. If you have a piano, once every two or three years you have to have some chap in to tune it. But because a harpsichord is so delicate, you have to 'voice' it (ie tune it) about every week, unlike a piano which is tuned once in two or three years. And in order to voice it you have to understand how it works.

If you buy something (unless it's a hammer) you don't know how it works. You have to build it yourself in order to know what makes it go. The basic alienation between people and the technological devices we buy, is largely from the fact that we don't know how they work and how they operate. Now what happens if people do begin to build things for themselves?

Well - in the USA the largest colour television set that people can obtain (by the way I'm not suggesting that's a good thing) - but the largest one they can obtain only comes in kit form. People build it for themselves. The interesting thing is that these people then become voluntary television repairmen in their area because they're about the only people in the small town or village who understand how it works.

So we began to experiment to see what would happen if we de-classified vast numbers of objects and made them come in two ways - the way they do now and in do-it-your-self kits - things such as spin dryers, washers, and so forth. By the way let me point out to you that, based on my experience with Volvo, I might suggest that any one of you can build a safer, better Fiat 126 than is being built by the workers at Fiat, who are hung-over, disgusted, don't like their work, pay little attention to it and tend from time to time to sabotage the work out of sheer boredom. You are experts. But the difficulty is that Fiat 126's don't come in kit form - as yet.

'ALTERNATIVE'

I thought that we should make a formal bow to 'alternative' design and architecture. I show you Steve Beer's house in Albuquerque, New Mexico. It's full of self-activating freon-gas filled tubes that raise and lower the windows, and the famous fifty-five gallon oil-drum block-bodied wall, filled with water to conduct heat from the outside to the inside.

FEEDBACK

Feedback seems to be something designers don't care about at all. Some months ago when I was in the city of Chicago on a brief visit I was taken to a new building there which tends to sway a great deal. It's the tallest building in Chicago. The architect who did it asked me what I thought of it. I said I found the swaying of the building remarkably unpleasant and I was aware of the fact that in the USA a new medical speciality now exists - which is to take care of the people who are made sick by the fact that the building in which they work rocks and sways. And this architect said, 'As far as I'm concerned the building only has to stand still for 1/125 second at f5.6'.

I'd like to show you one or two things that have to do with feedback. Here is a pill safe designed by a student of mine about ten years ago in the USA to keep pills and medicines out of the reach of small children. It works marvellously well but it turned out to be very expensive. So a redesign was done. We now have a whole series of these boxes which are difficult for children to open. Well that's fine - the problem is solved. In Canada, the USA, Sweden, Denmark and a number of other countries prescription drugs can only be sold with that kind of closure. So what's the feedback situation? Well, the feedback is that the children who used to take tranquillisers, the pill or what-have-you, now drink laundry detergent, soap and various other things and kill or maim themselves in that manner. So what is needed then, is some sort of box that can be locked so that children can't get in. But it shouldn't be locked with a key because in the same house there may be an older person who has heart trouble and immediately needs his heart drugs, or is blind, or arthritic, or something of that nature.

So what we did in Denmark was to design a series of boxes that could only be opened by grown-ups because of the ergonomic limitations of a child's hand - so that even an arthritic elderly person can get it open while a little child can't.

Now the final point is the political strategy. In this case it was not to design the boxes, but to use them as a tool to hold a press conference. They were included in a television show - and after about one and a half years there was in fact a law passed in Denmark which means that a box of this sort, that can only be opened by adults, must be in every flat and every house that is offered for rent or sale.

But now moving to Britain from Denmark I found myself struck with the question - what can you possibly do in England (where laws almost never change)? A student at Manchester took this to the third stage which was to design a do-it-yourself plug-in locking mechanism that can go into any sort of cabinet and again is controlled by the ergonomic considerations of the human hand.

And that brings me to the end of the formal part of my presentation ...

THE FUTURE OF DESIGN EDUCATION
Prof. Bruce Archer and Ken Baynes

The paper presented to the conference by Ken Baynes was based on the material which follows, itself an edited version of papers presented to the Design in General Education Summer School, Royal College of Art, July 1976 by Professor Bruce Archer.

The research project Design in General Education is an enquiry into the nature, value, organisation and problems of design awareness as a subject for study in general education. The aim is to produce a description of what is happening in schools; to evaluate and report on current and possible future practice; to identify possible strategies for the future; and to make recommendations for a mechanism to co-ordinate development.

This prescription for our task did not take the form it did by accident. In order to understand what lay behind it, it is necessary to go back beyond the start of our study and to examine briefly the events and pressures which led to its inception. Here it is possible to identify three main themes.

> There existed a grass roots movement in schools, based on the idea that something called 'Design Studies' constituted a new way of handling art, craft, environmental studies, technology, home economics or parts of those. Also that such studies could be a new way of handling other subjects like civics, the quality of life and so on.

> There existed an idea which had arisen originally in the 'consumer field' that design studies were an important way of improving discrimination and raising the standards of design generally. By the 'consumer field' I do not only mean consumer goods, but town planning, architecture, engineering, graphics and so on. Many people who were worried about low environmental standards believed that since so many of the decisions which affect our environment and the quality of life are made by elected members on local authority committees, or by accountants and managers, these people needed to have some experience of the relevant qualities and criteria. They were also arguing that one of the reasons why things went wrong in our cities and in the things that we used and bought was that those who needed to co-operate with architects, planners and designers were very often unable to perceive, appreciate and understand the arguments put forward by them. The next step was to say therefore, that design studies were necessary for many other professions besides the design professions. Probably lawyers, accountants and managing directors all needed an element of design studies in their education in order to conduct their affairs correctly and so serve the

community more effectively.

Finally, there existed an idea which had arisen in the professional designer's field. It was a concern with the problems
of the environment: a concern with pollution, the depletion of
resources, with 'spaceship earth'. In this context, many
professional designers had been disturbed by their traditional
role, which for many of them had been closely related with
consumption and growth, and with change and fashion. They
were wondering what were the new ethics to which the design
professions should direct themselves if conservation was
going to become more important, if growth was to be contra-
indicated, and if change for the sake of change was socially
undesirable.

All these themes were interacting. Many had been in people's minds for a long time.
They reached a new urgency in 1968 when Paul Ehrlich drew attention in a dramatic
way to the prospects before us. During 1972 and 1973 there were innumerable
national and international conferences and seminars set up by various bodies to
investigate one or other of the three themes. Amongst them were two series in
Great Britain, one organised by the Department of Education and Science, the other
by the Design Council, which brought together all three areas of concern. After
several meetings of the interested parties, who had been brought together on the
immediate initiative of the Director of the Design Council Sir Paul Reilly, the
Secretary of State for Education of the day agreed to finance a two-year study
looking into the problem. And so we came into being and had the particular brief
which I have already described.

What have we found out? I can refer here to five points which appear to have great
importance for the future and upon which we shall have to base any suggestions about
future strategy.

Our research has confirmed our original impression that there
is a grass roots movement for design in general education.
It is not always called design, it goes under other names in
some schools, and not everything which is called design
appears to be part of that grass roots movement. Nevertheless
we believe the movement is real, is very widespread and
already has considerable momentum.

There is evidence to suggest that there is now a sufficient
body of knowledge for the area called 'design' to be developed
to a level which will merit scholarly regard for the future.

It appears that design education in schools, being necessarily
child-centred and geared to child development, will differ in
many important respects from adult concerns with design,
adult concepts of what design is, adult structures and adult
procedures. A mere translation into the classroom of what

we believe architects and designers to be doing is not a
desirable or adequate way of dealing with design education in
schools.

It is important for all of us to recognise that design education
is not a panacea for society's or education's ills. In particular:
it is not an answer to problems of school organisations or
resource allocation; it is not just a rag-bag substitute for an
uncomfortably growing list of art, civics, urban studies, etc;
it is not just a euphemistic way of describing the studies open
to the less academic or more practical child.

Our evaluation of past and current curriculum development
projects and implementation policies suggest that local,
teacher-conducted, inter-school development and implementation is both practicable and desirable; not only because
this befits a grass roots movement, but also because the
evidence is that this is an efficient way of bringing about
implementation.

In conjunction with the work which was involved in establishing these basic points, we
have also tried to develop a better set of concepts and related terminology. This
has been done in collaboration with teachers and other educationalists and in the
context of the knowledge about the nature of the design which already exists in my
own department. The aim has been to introduce a higher degree of definition into
the terminology we use and, as a result, to make it possible to distinguish between
the various components that appear to be important in any discussion of design in
general education.

There is emerging general agreement that in its broadest sense the word 'Design' can
be used with a big D in the same way that 'Science' can be used with a big S, and that
in this context it indicates the whole of the human concern, activity and knowledge that
has to do with moulding the environment. This provides the top definition in a pyramid.
As a group, the definitions that we have developed work out as follows:

DESIGN is the area of human experience, skill and knowledge
that reflects man's concern with the appreciation and adaptation
of his surroundings in the light of his material and spiritual
needs. In particular, it relates with configuration, composition,
meaning, value and purpose in man-made phenomena. (Analogous
with Humanities, Science) Hence:

DESIGN AWARENESS is design as philosophy. It is conscious-
ness of configuration, composition, meaning, value and
purpose in man-made phenomena and the ability to understand
and handle ideas related with them. (Analogous with literacy
and numeracy)

DESIGN ACTIVITY is design as an art. It is the set of skills
by which man adapts things to suit him better. (Analogous with
technology, skill)

DESIGN EDUCATION is the mechanism effecting the
transmission of the body of ideas, information and technique
which constitutes the received state of knowledge and skill.
It may be concerned primarily with design awareness or it
may be concerned primarily with design activity. Most often
it will contain some of both.

Further sub-divisions are possible, for example:

Under design DESIGN AWARENESS:

DESIGN SENSIBILITY, which is the development of the ability
to discriminate different kinds and degrees of configuration,
order, value, purpose and meaning.

DESIGN HISTORY, which, like natural history, represents
not only the study of design phenomena in the past, but also a
systematic account of how things come to be the way they are.

Under DESIGN ACTIVITY:

DESIGN SCIENCE, which is the body of knowledge that is
significant for the understanding of design phenomena and for
the pursuit of design activity.

DESIGN CRAFT, which is the skill and technique that is
significant for the handling of design phenomena and for the
exercise of design activity.

And under DESIGN EDUCATION:

DESIGN STUDIES, which are specific learning experiences
related with design awareness or design activity.

DESIGN RESEARCH, which is systematic enquiry calculated
to produce knowledge significant for design awareness or
design activity.

When we look at humanities, we find that many people will argue that the core subject
is language, and the body of knowledge is literature. In science the core subject
might be said to be mathematics while the body of knowledge is the laws within which
the mathematical mode is applied. In those terms, I would argue that the body of
knowledge in design is the man-made habitat: architecture, the contents of the Victoria
and Albert Museum, what is in the galleries and fashion shows, in the street, in the
home and in the factory. It is there - not in books, but all around. I would go on to
say that our core subject is modelling. This is borne out by the theoretical work
going on elsewhere. Here I am using the term model in a very strict sense of the word:

A model is something which stands for or represents something
else. Modelling is the making or using of models. A model
could be a drawing, a plan, imagery, a form of words, a
chemical or mathematical formula, a diagram, a complex
construction in wood or metal - anything which is used to

stand for or represent something else.

Why do we use models? We may wish to represent, in a simpler, cheaper or safer
form, something which already exists in a complex form in order to capture its
essence - to clarify, to probe, to manipulate, to experiment with, to understand, to
remember, to preserve. We may also wish to represent in model form something
which exists only in our imagination, in order to communicate, to consolidate, to
elaborate, to test, to build. Thoughts can be said to be internal or cognitive models
of ideas or things. Our utterances are external or descriptive models of those
thoughts. Designs are prescriptive models of the way we would like things to be.
We may or may not then be able to take action to cause things to become like the
model we have prescribed. In these terms a culinary recipe is a design. So is a
musical or chorological score. These, together with flow charts, computer
programmes and knitting patterns, are a special kind of design called algorithms,
which describe not the end product but the set of actions to be taken in order to
produce the desired result. A piece of sculpture or a work of art, on the other hand,
is the result itself. It is a direct, external representation of something in the artist's
heart and mind. Mime is a similar sort of model. Film and television presentations
are models of actual or supposed happenings, displayed as changing patterns of light
on a screen. Our eyes form perceptual models of the apparent happenings. Our
minds form cognitive models of the meaning of those perceptions. In response,
we may construct our own design in the form of a letter telling the author or television
company exactly what we think should be done about it.

It is possible, of course, to describe, understand and prescribe suggested changes
in the world of things through the medium of the languages of words or mathematical
notation. There are some aspects of the world of things and of man's relations with
them which cannot be so described. The core subject of the discipline of design is
the set of languages used to describe, evaluate and adapt the world of things. The
term 'modelling' is applied to describe this set of languages.

Turning to the question of the test which must be applied in order to recognise a
piece of knowledge as belonging to the field of design, I offer the following answers:
Knowledge in the design field is characterised by being:

> Anthropocentric (the 'habitat' or 'human' aspect)
>
> Discriminatory (the 'feeling' or 'judging' aspect)
>
> Operational (the 'doing' or 'forming' aspect)

By anthropocentric, I mean design's essential concern with man, his environment and
his activities, as compared with (say) mathematics, which seeks to be fundamental
and abstract. By discriminatory, I mean design's essential concern with comparison
and value, for example in ethics, meaning, aesthetics, utility, comfort, convenience
or safety, as compared with (say) chemistry, which seeks to be as free as practicable
from value-judgement. By operational, I mean design's concern with choosing,
planning, arranging, adapting, forming and making, as compared with (say) geography
which seeks to describe rather than to effect. Under these three tests, almost all
that goes on in the art rooms and craft workshops in schools belongs to the design

field, together with most environmental studies, much home economics, some technical and civic studies, and possibly dance and music.

The last thing we have to do is to translate the analysis of factual research and theoretical speculation into much more specific alternatives for future development. Here our thoughts are at their most tentative. As I see it, there are seven courses of action or roads open to us, any of which we might follow:

1 To develop design studies (design awareness or design activity or both) as an additional subject in the school curriculum.

2 To develop design activity as a learning method in the approach to any suitable subject (including, for example, reading and number).

3 To develop design awareness as an element in the analysis of any suitable subject.

4 To accept the term 'design studies' as a new name for, transformation of, or merging of existing subjects such as art, craft, home economics, technical studies etc.

5 To recognise and encourage the creation of design faculties as a way of providing an organisational structure for the management of the 'practical' subjects.

6 To recognise and encourage the creation of design centres as locations for grouped or combined resources for 'practical' subjects.

7 To use Design as the generic term for a given segment of human experience, skill and knowledge (comparable to Science or Humanities) and to develop educational approaches in relation to this broad concept.

It is my personal view that we should reject and resist road Four. I take a very negative view of using 'design studies' as a term which transforms the existing subjects, or simply gives them a new name. We need something far more substantial and less damaging than that.

I take a conditionally negative view of roads Five, Six and Seven. By conditionally negative I mean that I would regard these directions as counter-productive if they were to be pursued alone.

That leaves us with the top three alternatives. I take a conditionally positive view of roads One and Two. That is to say, I regard design studies as an additional subject to be all-right but insufficient, and I regard design activity as a learning method anywhere throughout school to be all-right but insufficient.

What I would personally hope to see emerge is a combination of roads Seven and Three. That is to say, we recognise that there is this area of human knowledge, experience

and skill to which we can give this generic name, but that we also urge design awareness as an element in the analysis of every subject. To achieve this we would need
to make it clear that design implies an attitude, a set of values, and a way of looking
at things, that are of profound general relevance. I believe this could be done.

I recognise, however, that it is very unlikely that anyone could travel roads Three
and Seven without support from roads One and Two or both. So it is very likely that,
if we are going to achieve our aim, at least some schools will need to include design
on their timetables as a specific subject and to develop their skill in encouraging
design activities. Some will also find that roads Five and Six can suitably and quickly
be expanded to provide the necessary institutional framework within which the work of
development can be carried out. The implications of all these findings will be pursued
in our report to the Secretary of State for Education.

CONCLUDING ADDRESS
Lord Esher

'The second generation homo faber does not perceive the world in terms of things, but in terms of needs to be satisfied: this is the prosaic challenge for future industrial design'. I start this brief and I'm afraid inevitably inadequate sum-up with those words of Gui Bonsiepe's because I think they put our collective view in one sentence.

One of Karl Marx's best known aphorisms was that what mattered was not to understand the world but to change it. All the same, he set about understanding it first - and this is a thing that designers are bored by and bad at, and they get virtually no help from most of the schools they go to. So I start with a shorthand sum-up of our world towards the end of the century, as it has emerged from some of the expert papers presented to this Conference.

One can identify three great areas of need. First is resource conservation and overriding, because we have to eat, is to conserve the world's minutely thin crust of topsoil and to use it more intelligently, which in present conditions has to mean more intensively. This is as true of Britain as it is of Bangladesh. A six-lane motorway in Oxfordshire that is grossly underloaded, a low-density new city in Bucks on good farmland because political pressures drove it off heathlands in Hampshire: these are ecological crimes. It may cost £75,000 to put one new dwelling into dockland (if one includes the infrastructure) but that is where it has to go, and the rest of the problem is to cut that cost by better thinking. And having protected the topsoil, we have to put more people on to it, and so do what we can to reduce the pull of the cities.

Unfortunately, it won't be a great many more people. Otto Königsberger, in a recent lecture at University College London, said that land redistribution in the Third World would only increase its holding capacity by 10%.

Every year until the end of the century, he said, a population equal to that of the whole of the UK will move into the world's exploding cities - that is 1,300 million by the year 2000. So this is our second great area of need. Current enlightened thinking is that this can only be met by do-it-yourself housing, but it goes against the grain with most designers to see it happen in this messy way. I quote from Ivan Illich:

> 'There is a normal course for those who make development
> policies, whether they live in North or South America, in
> Russia or Israel. It is to define development and to set its
> goals in ways with which they are familiar, which they are
> accustomed to use in order to satisfy their own needs, and
> which permit them to work through the institutions over which
> they have power to control. This formula has failed, and
> must fail. There is not enough money in the world for

133

> development to succeed along these lines. ' (For money,
> of course, read resources.)

He's right about the failure.   There was an excellent example a few years back in
Lima, where an international ideas competition was held for barriada housing.   All
the great names took part, including our own Mr Stirling, but how could they be
expected to get inside the mind of the user, a descendant of the forever withdrawn
and alienated Inca culture?   It was a communication gap typical of our age, and I'll be
coming back to it.   For a moment one can only say that it's unlikely that European
designers will contribute a great deal to this gigantic coral-reef-type building enterprise, despite it's being the greatest work effort ever undertaken by the human race...
unless they change their spots.

Which brings me to the third area of need - much nearer home.   I come home because
I profoundly believe that each of the different kinds of society Victor Papanek enumerated
has its own problem, and the best thing one can do is to attach one's own.

In his recent 'Second Look at Doom' Lord Ashby speculated on the effects of the
economic/political stranglehold which the world's commodity producers, pioneered
by OPEC, can now exert on our First World, if one should call it that.   He saw these
effects as fundamentally political.   Whereas natural ecosystems are, contrary to
popular belief, wonderfully resilient and capable of recovering from disturbances,
'man-made systems by contrast, have evolved in complexity without a corresponding
evolution of stability'.   He took the fragility of New York as an example, and he
went on:

> 'The tempting way to resolve such tension is by autocracy and
> force.   If you could shoot, or put in jail, or even sack and
> starve, dissident citizens (and of course there are nations
> where you could do any of these) the symbiotic stability of
> human ecosystems could be maintained - after a fashion.   In
> fact this is the way we stabilised our own society in the 1840's.
> But the social conscience has evolved a long way since then.
>
> Our dilemma is that the welfare state, which is a by-product
> of the consumer society, despite its enormous benefits, has
> undoubtedly weakened the stability of symbiosis in human
> communities.   But to respond by going back to autocracy,
> dictatorship, totalitarianism, would be a shameful atavism. '

It's easy for my generation to say, atavistically, that we managed it in the war, when
we got as near as we ever have to a fully controlled economy with public consent.
But the public consent was strictly temporary ('for the duration' was the phrase).
It was temporary, and it was exploitative: as soldiers we lived off the country - license
vandals and pilferers.   One can't escape the dilemma that way.   It's no exaggeration
to say that this island is likely to be the place where the First World's capacity to
resolve this dilemma will be tested.

The first test will be unemployment.   We have to assume that there is never going
to be enough work to go round.   Mary McCarthy, in her novel 'Birds of America',

makes her hero reflect that 'if the right to work became the privilege of a few, that would be just as unjust as having leisure as a privilege of a few. What was good about the Middle Ages was that everybody worked: the knight fought, the peasant ploughed, the lady cooked - even a cat had a job. ' Of course they were all part time, which was hopelessly inefficient. Hence the invention of the division of labour, to which Marxists attribute all the iniquities of capitalism. Adam Smith anticipated them in an often-quoted passage:

> 'In opulent and commercial societies ... to think or to reason
> comes to be, like every other employment, a particular
> business, which is carried on by a very few people who furnish
> the public with all the thought and reason possessed by the
> vast multitudes that labour. '

And here, in that mirror, we contemplate ourselves, with professional affixes after our names, brass plates on our doors, and a smart receptionist inside - that's one image. The alternative image is ... let's call him the barefoot designer, a worker like any other, with no middle class pretensions, but with a role as central as the milkman's. His role is wholly without egotism, to help communities or families or any association of human beings to get it together, to satisfy their will to form (to use the catch-phrases of two different generations). Let's take it slowly at this point, because we have reached what I believe to be the fundamental conflict in our society. It has nothing to do with conventional politics: neither of our big political parties is much interested, and that's why so many of us don't belong to either of them.

The controversy about grammar schools and comprehensives, the confrontations in the universities, the disruptions of motorway inquiries, the rows in the Health Service, the backlash against the modernist utopia, the Architects' Revolutionary Council, the Street Farmers, every planning battle from Tolmer's Square to Covent Garden - they are all about one issue, and the issue is this: Are we still bound by that social contract by which the common man, in exchange for a higher standard of living, accepted the authority and the values of the educated elite, because this was the only known way of getting that higher standard? Obviously most socialist and capitalist societies are absolutely bound by it, and most hippie communes and other drop-out communities are parasitic upon it. Yet the mediaeval dream keeps coming back, particularly in the Anglo-Saxon countries; or to put it negatively, we experts are beginning to feel less certain we know how people ought to live. Amateurs, who have been happily performing music and painting pictures and writing poems for centuries, might - it is felt - be quite good with their environment too.

Ken Baynes, to whom I owe this line of thought, believes that the breakout from that social contract may come in our own field of design. Just as the printing press destroyed the authority of the universal church, so he believes the teaching of design in general education will undermine the authority of the planner, the social engineer, the architect and the fashion expert. People will know just enough to do it themselves: they'll grow houses the way they do vegetables, swopping tools and know-how, with Snug the joiner, and Bottom the weaver, and all the rest of them back in their village roles, respected craftsmen living by bartering skills as indeed they still do in most

of the world's urban communities. It didn't work for William Morris because in his
England high technology looked a better prospect. Now we are back with him, whether
we like it or not. I mention Snug the joiner because we must face the fact that most of
the propaganda for the alternative life-style has a strong element of the absurd. But
even if it hadn't, or when it hasn't, it has got to face one serious psychological as well
as all the obvious economic objections. This is that throughout history man has equated
civilisation with order, with calm and above all, with cleanliness. Squalor, however
cheerful, equalled barbarism. And when one adds to the litter after the pop festival
the frightful growth of teenage violence in the streets, it's not surprising if the life
of the new world looks unenticing. It's equally unappealing to people who want to get
on with their own work rather than spend half their lives discussing what the community
ought to do.

We may agree that Design for Need is not something middle class people ought to do
for the workers, or whites for blacks, or producers for consumers, but let's have no
illusions about the pains and frustrations of design by discussion. They can only be
sustained by a burning faith that this is the wave of the future, the logical complement
of comprehensive education and the welfare state. I imagine that most of us are here
because we share, if not that faith, at any rate that hope, and moreover have a feeling,
as I have, that to demonstrate that non-paternalist decision-making can work in a free
society could be this country's next contribution to civilisation.

But of course this can't be the end of what I say, because another equally urgent task
confronts all designers - equally urgent, and equally demanding. This is to play our
part in the renewal of our country's industries, to get into the new-style, much more
imaginative growth business, without which nothing in this country is going to work.
We don't live, as many of the young would like to think, between two worlds, 'one dead,
the other powerless to be born', but in two worlds, both necessary, both struggling to
be born. But so the human race always has: it has always needed its knights as well as
its cooks - not to mention its cats.

It sticks out a mile doesn't it, that the world doesn't only need fairer shares; it needs
more to share out - more medical schools, more dams, more weeks at the seaside.
These things have to be bought, and in this country we get our wealth, as we have
always got it, by ingenuity. So in the end Design for Need equals Need for Design.
But that's another story.

Or is it? Are we not a little naive and priggish in the distinction we draw between
socially OK and anti-social design? It reminds me of the snobbish attitude of housing
architects to the spec builder. The Sunday colour supplements, so shocking to the
sensitive eye of the puritanical, reflect the market economy as accurately as the interv
semi-Ds now so lovingly portrayed by David Hepher. By this market economy, by its
innocence as well as its guilt, by its bad taste as well as its good, we support a welfare
state in an open society. One man's wants support another man's needs. Designers
have to be in both camps, minding their own business of innovation, reconciliation and
economy. If they are good and only if they are good, it's a battle both sides can win.

And what do I mean by 'good'? When Lethaby was asked this question he pointed to an
example, to the new 'Safety Bicycle' as it was called which was one of the real joys of

Edwardian life, and is (with the pill) still the world's best example of Design for Need. And since I have mentioned Lethaby I will end with some words of his:

> 'So many look on Art and Music from the mere spectator's
> point of view, as if they were things to be admired, or not,
> by him. But true Art is the evidence of the workman's joy in
> his work. Art should be looked on not as luxury and enjoyment
> to the buyer but as life and breath to the maker, and extend the
> idea to cover everything of quality and goodness in things made
> by hands, and further, to beautiful care of the tilled earth. Art
> should be everywhere. It cannot exist in isolation or one-man
> thick; it must be a thousand men thick.'

He was speaking - and I am speaking - of a new industrial revolution, or what Sir Brian Flowers called, using words that were significant coming from a man like him, 'a reorientation of our technological society and a switch to high quality labour-intensive production'.

How do such movements start? Asa Briggs said that they start not by technical change, but by a change in the moral climate, such as the one we can see happening around us in this country: we have this role thrust upon us by our society's plain refusal to live any longer in the world created by the division of labour. And where do such movements start? They start nowadays, I suggest, in the free universities. No wonder, as Professor Briggs told us, that governments take an ambivalent view of universities. They know that our job is first to understand the world and then to change it. Let there be no underestimating the size of the job: it is far too big for designers. In institutional and UK terms, it would mean the coming together of the best thinking we can bring to bear here in the Royal College of Art, at the London School of Economics and down the road at the Imperial College of Science and Technology.

Meanwhile we can begin to live it, as some of you are doing, even in the midst of the old world and among the monuments of its failures as well as its successes. This Conference has been a milestone on your road, and not one of you has wasted your time in coming to it.

138

INDEX OF AUTHORS

ARCHER, L Bruce (1922, Gt Britain) CBE DrRCA CEng MIMechE MIED ASIA
Professor in Department of Design Research, Royal College of Art, London. Member
of Design Council. External Examiner for Open University and Council for National
Academic Awards. Lecturer: Ashridge Management College; London College of
Furniture. 'Systematic Method for Designers' published 1964 (HMSO). Member of
the Design for Need Organising Committee. Paper: (read by Ken Baynes).

BAYNES, Ken (1934, Gt Britain)
Trained as a Painter and studied stained glass design at the Royal College of Art.
Assistant Editor of Graphis in Zürich. Research Fellow, Department of Design
Research, RCA. Designer for King Edward's Hospital Fund for London; Welsh Arts
Council; Lund Humphries, etc. Author of books on Art and Society, Hospital Design
and Evaluation, Design Education. Television programmes on Design Education.
Paper: The Future of Design Education (delivered on behalf of Bruce Archer).

BONSIEPE, Gui (1934, Germany)
Head of Product Development Section, Instituto Nacional de Tecnologia Industrial,
Libertad 1235, Buenos Aires. Studied at the Hochschule für Gestaltung, Ulm 1955-59.
Teaching and research at the HfG, until 1968. Multilateral technical assistance project
in Chile until 1970. Head of the Product Development Group at the Institute for
Technological Investigations, Chile 1971-73. Publications: Diseño Industrial; Artefacto
y Proyecto (Madrid, 1975); Teoria e practica del disegno industriale (Feltrinelli, Milan
1975). Paper: Precariousness and Ambiguity - Industrial Design in Dependent Countries.

BRADEN, Su (1943, Gt Britain)
48 Denman Road, London SE15. Trained in Fine Art (Sculpture) at Maidstone and
Goldsmith's Colleges. Co-founder of Pavilions in the Parks, 1967-70. Currently
researching a book about art and the community. Visual Arts Editor of Time Out since
1971, and working with the Walworth and Aylesbury Community Arts Group in South
East London. Paper: The Artist as Producer. Exhibit: Flyovers can be Fun for Skaters.

CORNFORD, Christopher Francis (1917, Gt Britain)
Draughtsman, Painter, Chelsea School of Art, 1933-35. Taught at King's College,
University of Durham, 1946-50; Cambridge University School of Architecture, 1955-62;
Cambridgeshire College of Arts and Technology, 1958-62. Professor of General Studies,
Royal College of Art, London since 1962. Articles in British Journal of Aesthetics,
Design Magazine, Times Literary and Educational Supplements, Leonardo etc. Book
on Proportion Theory in preparation. Interested in ecology, alternative technology,
community organisations, art education and art patronage. Design for Need Symposium
Organiser.

DICKSON, David (1947, Gt Britain)
Graduate in mathematics. Features Editor, The Times Higher Educational Supplemen
New Printing House Square, Grays Inn Road, London WC1. Member of the Editorial
Collective of 'Radical Science Journal'. Author of 'Alternative Technology and the
Politics of Technical Change' (Fontana, London 1974). Paper: Technology - The
Language of Social Action.

ESHER, Lionel, Viscount, (1913, Gt Britain) CBE MA PPRIBA FILA
Architect, Planner, Landscapist specialising in new town planning, housing and centra
city planning. Rector and Vice-Provost of the Royal College of Art, London. Author
of books and articles on architecture, housing and landscape. Chairman of the Design
for Need Advisory Council. Paper: Concluding Address.

FLOWERS, Sir Brian Hilton (1924, Gt Gritain) MA DSc FRS
Bishop Gore Grammar School, Swansea. Gonville and Caius College (Exhibitioner),
Cambridge; Hon Fellow 1974. University of Birmingham. Chief Research Scientist,
Atomic Energy Research Establishment, 1958. Rector, Imperial College of Science
and Technology, South Kensington, London SW7. Chairman, Science Research Counci
1967-73. President: Institute of Physics, 1972-74; European Science Foundation.
Chairman: joint working group on computers for research, 1965. Chairman, Royal
Commission on Environment Pollution. Editor, Advances in Physics, 1959-63;
Cambridge Monograph, 1962-66. Publications: (with E Mendoza) Properties of Matter,
1970; various contributions to scientific periodicals on the structure of the atomic
nucleus, on nuclear reactions, and on science policy. Paper: Opening Address.

GOMEZ, Alfonso (1948, Chile) MDesRCA
Architect and Engineer, Department of Design Research, Royal College of Art,
London. Paper: The Need for Design Education in Developing Countries.

HALL, Janet (1951, Gt Britain) MA(RCA)
Designer and ergonomist to the Department of Health and Social Security. Concerned
with fire precautions in hospitals, hygiene unit for the disabled and able-bodied, and
mobility toys for children. Paper: Ergonomic Analysis of Personal Hygiene Activities.

HAWKINS, Oliver (1944, Gt Britain)
MA in Architecture and Fine Arts at Cambridge University. Design Management,
Michael Farr (Design Integration) Ltd; Allied International Designers Ltd. Industrial
Design/Design Management, West Sussex College of Design, Union Place, Worthing,
Sussex. Major teaching interest: industrial liaison. Major professional interest:
the designer's identity crisis. Paper: Person to Person Design.

HEIGHT, Frank (1921, Gt Britain) DesRCA CEng MIMechE FSIA
Consultant Industrial Designer and Engineer. Co-ordinator, ICSID Working Group III
on Education. Co-ordinator of first ICSID Interdesign Seminars, USSR 1971; Ireland
1972. Professor of Industrial Design, Royal College of Art, London. Joint Chairman
of the Design for Need Organising Committee.

JOSHI, Raghunath Krishna (1937, India)
'Shoneel', Devna Road, Bombay 400088. Art Director and Director, Ulka Advertising

Pvt. Ltd, Bombay. Visiting Lecturer in calligraphy and typography respectively at
the Sir J J School of Arts and the Sir J J Institute of Applied Art. Has delivered various
lectures on Devanagari including a series of four lectures, in 1974, on Aesthetics of
Letterform, for the Aesthetics Society of Bombay. Participant in IDCA, 1969, as
delegate from India. Designer of decimal series stamp, 1956; Ramcharit Manas stamp,
1975; and Bahadur Shah Jafar stamp, 1975. Has received several awards for advertising
campaigns, symbols and corporate identity plans. Has staged Multilingual Happenings
(in 1970); Demographic Happenings (in 1971); and Musical Happenings (in 1975). Concrete
poet, practising calligrapher and designer of the Devanagari script. Paper:
Deshanagari - A Common Script for All Indian Languages.

KUBY, Thomas (1941, Germany)
Studied Industrial Design at Illinois Institute of Technology, Chicago; Hochschule für
Gestaltung, Ulm (Diploma); and the Royal College of Art (MDes) 1970-72. Work with
ITDG, development of egg-tray machine. Lecturer in technology and politics at
University of Bremen, 2800 Bremen 33. Paper: Social Forces Determine the Shape of
Technology.

LASSUS, Bernard (1929, France)
Professor, Department of Architecture, l'Ecole Nationale Superieure des Beaux-Arts,
80 rue Vercingetorix, Paris 14e. Member of the Haut Comité de l'Environment.
Responsible for the Centre de Recherche d'Ambiances as director of research into the
use of imagery, particularly that of suburb dwellers, in the personalisation of the
territory between plot boundary and facade around the detached house; including
certain practical projects in landscape and layout in new towns and redeveloped areas
of established habitats. Paper: Le Démesurable. Exhibit: Paysage Global ou
Démesurable.

LLOYD-JONES, Peter BSc PhD ARCS
Head of School of Three-Dimensional Design, Kingston Polytechnic, Kingston-upon-
Thames, Surrey. Paper: Tourism at Stonehenge. Radio Talk: Designing for Need.

MANOY, Russell (1945, New Zealand) MSc (Ergonomics: Loughborough)
Wellington School of Design, NZ 1963-65. Post-graduate Industrial Design, Central
School, London 1966-69. Consultant Designer since 1969. Anthropometric Survey for
British Rail - Applied Ergonomics. Teacher at Ravensbourne College of Art and
Design and at the Royal College of Art, London. Paper: A Range of Easy Chairs for the
Disabled Adult and Elderly Frail. Exhibit: Tableware for the Handicapped.

MITCHELL, John (1937, Gt Britain) BA (Psychology) MSc (Ergonomics - London)
Member of Chartered Society of Physiotherapy. Papers at ERS, BES and Conference of
Yugoslav Ergonomic Society. Professional interests: disability ergonomics, particularly concerning children and mobility problems; development and production of low
handicap equipment and environments. Institute for Consumer Ergonomics, Loughborough University of Technology, Loughborough, Leics LE11 3TU. Paper: Low
Handicap Technology - the Reduction of Need by Design.

MURLIS, John
Apprenticeship and Systems Engineer in aircraft industry; fluid mechanics research

at Imperial College, post-graduate degree. Studied insect migration at the Centre for Overseas Pest Research. Member of the London Technical Group, 41 Queen's Gate, London SW7. Design studies in disaster shelter and anthropometric measurement. Paper: The Role of the Designer in Disaster Relief. Exhibit: Nutritional Assessment Equipment (with Ian Morton).

NADKARNI, Sudhakar S (1936, India)
Diploma in Visual Communication, Bombay; diploma in Industrial Design, Ulm. Director in an Advertising Agency in Bombay, with national awards in Visual Communication programme. Associate Professor at the National Institute of Design, Ahmedabad. Professor-in-Charge, Industrial Design Centre, Indian Institute of Technology, Bombay 400076. Member, Industrial Design Committee, Government of India. Member of ICSID Working Group IV. Chairman, ICSID Education Committee, Asian Sub-Group. Member, ICSID Working Group for the Developing Countries/Design Information Group. Paper: Identification of Design Problems in India.

NEWPORT, Roger MDesRCA ID(E)
Adviser, Indian Institute of Technology, 1970-71. Senior Lecturer in Related Studies at Wolverhampton Polytechnic, Wulfruna Street, Wolverhampton WV1 1LY. Paper: Design Collaboration at the IIT, New Delhi, India 1970-72 (with Roger Breakwell).

PAPANEK, Victor (1925, Austria) FSIA
Designer, anthropologist, writer, teacher and film-maker. Member of ICSID Working Group IV, Developing Countries. Has lived and worked in eleven countries, and designs for UNESCO/UNIDO in design management for developing countries. Senior Design Consultant to Volvo AB in Sweden, developing a taxi for the handicapped and creating 'Work Enrichment' programmes. After resigning from being Dean of the School of Design at CalArts, spent one year in Denmark and two years in England. Visiting Guest Professor at Carleton University in Ottawa. Publications: 'Design for the Real World' (translated into twenty-three languages); 'Nomadic Furniture' and 'Nomadic Furniture 2' (with Jim Hennessey); and 'How Things Don't Work', to be published in 1976. Paper: Twelve Methodologies for Design - Because People Count.

PRIEST, Keith (1950, Gt Britain) AA(Dip)
Award winner, Huddersfield Building Society Housing Competition, 1972. Commended, Roosevelt Island Housing Competition, New York 1975. Cinema Project published various magazines, 1975. Various industrial/commercial projects (UK/France) with Wolff Olins, 22 Dukes Road, London WC1 since 1974. Paper: After the Oil Boom - Design for a Service Centre.

QUEENSBERRY, David, Marquess of, (1929, Gt Britain) FSIA
Professor of Ceramics and Glass, Royal College of Art, London. Trained: Central School of Arts and Crafts; North Staffordshire College of Technology. Formed Queensberry/Hunt Design Partnership in 1966. Ceramics plant for the Research and Producitivity Council in New Brunswick, Canada; Diversification Programme for Doulton Insulators; Development and Research into ceramic techniques for Sanitary ware. 'The Designer, The Craftsman and The Manufacturer', RSA Journal, Jan 1976. Paper: Ceramics for the Developing World (with Abdul Gaffoor & Lynn Reeve).

SEMITI, Godfrey A (1931, Tanzania) BSc (Lon)
Ministry of National Education, Dar es Salaam. Plant Breeding and Genetics,
Cambridge, 1959-60. Plant Breeder, 1957-62. Senior Extension Officer, 1962-64.
Senior Research Officer, 1964-69. Director of Research and Training, Ministry of
Agriculture, 1969-74. Director of Food and Nutritition Centre, 1974. Food and
Agriculture Adviser, Ministry of Education since 1974. Has produced improved
genotypes of legumes and cashew nuts. Has worked on improvement of food and
nutrition in the Third World. Published papers on breeding and food and nutrition.
Paper: Some Aspects of Agrarian and Industrial Development in a Developing Country.

SMALLEY, John Malcolm (1949, Gt Britain)
Painter. Hinkley House, Badlesmere, Nr Faversham, Kent. Medway College of Art,
Brighton Polytechnic and the Royal College of Art, London. Currently German
scholarship holder. One of three painters in the Royal Marsden Hospital Project at
the RCA. Recently visited Sweden to study the country's attitude to art in hospitals.
Paper: The Role of the Artist in a Hospital Environment. Exhibit: The Royal Marsden
Hospital Project (with Dave Cashman, Ros Cuthbert and Peter Challis).

SMITH, Brian Reffin (1946, Gt Britain)
B Tech, Brunel University, 1968. Currently pursuing a Research Studentship in the
Department of Design Research, Royal College of Art, London. Concerned with art,
technology and society. A Director of the Institute for Research in Art and Technology.
Writer and broadcaster on aspects of computers (and technology in general) and society,
ranging from art through education to disaster relief. Paper: Conceptual Design -
A Polemic.

OTHER CONTRIBUTORS
TO THE DESIGN FOR NEED
EXHIBITION AND SYMPOSIUM

ABEND, C Joshua (1924, USA) BA
Vice-president Industrial Design Society of America. 831 James Street, Syracuse,
NY 13202, USA. Paper: The Design of Emergency and Disaster Related Equipment.
Exhibit: 1975 ARMCO Student Design Programme - work submitted by students repre-
senting Purdue University, Ohio State University, Rhode Island School of Design and
the University of Kentucky.

AHOLA, Jussi (1940, Finland)
Industrial Designer, Head Teacher of Industrial Design at the University of
Industrial Arts, Helsinki. Liisank, 7A8, 00170 Helsinki 17. Exhibit: Lung Function
Analyser.

AMT FUR INDUSTRIELLE FORMGESTALTUNG
Breite Strasse 11, 102 Berlin. Exhibits: by Ekkehard Punk, Wolfgang Schneider &
Jochen Schmieder, and Steffen Meier v Rouden at Hochschule für industrielle Form-
gestaltung, Halle; by Felicitas Kaufmann, Reinhard Tetzlaff and Jörg Grote at
Kunsthochschule, Berlin.

ANAND, Atha Vankar Uday (1945, India)
Teacher and Consultant with Industrial Design Centre, Indian Institute of Technology,
Powai, Bombay 400076. Exhibit: Rural Development Game.

BAKER, John Edward (1926, Gt Britain) BSc(Eng)
Senior Lecturer in Department of Mechanical Engineering, University of Technology,
Loughborough. Paper: The Design of a Solar Water Heating System.

BASSO, Mario (1947, Italy)
Architect. 44 Highgate Hill, London N19. Exhibit: A Strategy for Resettlement - Dagat
Dagatan Squatter Relocation, Manila (with Paul Mugnaioni).

BELTRAN, Felix
Art Director and Professor at the University of Havana, Apartado 4109, Zona 4,
Vedado, Habana, Cuba. Exhibit: Symbol for the Red Cross.

BERDEL, Dieter
Stiegengasse 8/27, A 1060, Wien, Austria. Paper: Designing for the Disabled: A New
Field of Work?

BERKHOUT, Karel J (1940, Netherlands)
Graphic Designer with GVN, Gerardusplein 9, Eindhoven, Netherlands. Exhibit:
Schipol Anti-noise Campaign.

BICKNELL, Julian (1945, Gt Britain)
MA DipArch from Cambridge School of Architecture 1968, Partner to Edward Cullinan
1968-72, Tutor in Schools of Environmental Design and Industrial Design, Royal
College of Art, London, Director of RCA Project Officer, Exhibition Organiser and
joint editor of Design for Need papers.

BIRCHALL HOLLOWAY & ASSOCIATES
Industrial Designers. 32 Beechwood Avenue, South Harrow, Middlesex. Exhibit:
Colour Sequence Learning Games.

BLACK, Sir Misha (1910, Russia) OBE RDI Hon DrRCA Hon D Tech
Architect and Industrial Designer. Senior Partner of Design Research Unit, 32 Aybrook
Street, London SW7 4QF. Emeritus Professor of Industrial Design at the Royal College
of Art. President, SIAD and ICSID. Joint Chairman of the Design for Need Organising
Committee.

BOCQUET, Gavin (1953, Gt Britain)
School of Industrial Design, Royal College of Art, London. Exhibit: Page Turner.

BOND, W T F
Chartered Engineer for the Medical Engineering Research Unit of Queen Mary's
Hospital for Children. 17 Crewes Lane, Warlingham, Surrey CR3 9NS. Paper:
Medical Engineering for the Disabled.

BRIGGS, Asa (1921, Gt Britain) MA BSc (Econ)
Historian. Provost of Worcester College, Oxford.

BRIGGS, Paul (1947, Gt Britain) DipAD BA
Lecturer, Furniture Design Research Unit, Department of Three-Dimensional Design,
Trent Polytechnic, Burton Street, Nottingham NG1 4BU. Exhibit: Mobiles for
Nottingham Children's Hospital (with Peter Vickers).

BRYER, Mike (1943, Gt Britain)
Sculptor, Tutor at Napier College, Edinburgh. 57 Greenhill Park, Penicuik, Midlothian
EH26 9EX. Exhibit: Rapidly erected portable structures for use in disaster situations,
agriculture and industry.

CAMDEN CASSETTE
14 Upper Park Road, London NW3 2UP. Exhibit: Camden Cassette - a talking newspaper
for the blind.

CASHMAN, David (1942, Gt Britain)
Painter, Tutor at the Royal College of Art, London. Organising Tutor for the Royal
Marsden Hospital Project.

CAUDURO/MARTINO ARQUITETOS ASSOCIADOS
Rue Prof Vital Palma e Silva 131, 01 455 Sao Paulo, Brasil. Exhibit: Sao Paulo Public
Transportation Graphics and street furniture system.

COUPLAND, Timothy Stephen (1951, Gt Britain)
Illustrator and Engineer, Middlesex Polytechnic (Hornsey College of Art), 17 South
Grove, London N15. Exhibit: The Nature of Design Education - cartoons.

CRITCHLOW, Keith (1933, Gt Britain)
Architect, Philospher, author of: 'Order in Space', 'Into the Hidden Environment',
'Islamic Pattern', 'Time Stands Still', Lecturer at the Architectural Association,
34-6 Bedford Square, London WC1. Paper: Attitudes and Actualities in Emergency
Housing.

CUTHBERT, Rosalind (1951, Gt Britain)
Department of Painting, Royal College of Art, London. Exhibit: The Royal Marsden
Hospital Project.

DAVIES, Glyn (1947, Gt Britain)
DipArch with Commendation, Leicester School of Architecture, 1972. Worked as local
authority architect for two years before getting involved with Bath Arts Workshop, a
community arts organisation supported by the Arts Council. Co-ordinator of BAW's
Video Project for one year; now officially self-employed on community architectural
aid service and lecturing. Research project: Experimental Fish Farm incorporating
AT. Co-founder of Community Technology, (Comtek). Paper/exhibit: Community
Technology.

DAWKINS, Ann (1948, Gt Britain)
Design for Need Secretary, Royal College of Art, London.

DAY, Michael (1937, Gt Britain)
Chaplain, Royal College of Art, London. Paper: Playing for Survival.

DICKINSON, Andrew (1954, Gt Britain)
Department of Three-Dimensional Design, North Staffordshire Polytechnic, College
Road, Stoke-on-Trent. Exhibit: Domestic Refuse Separation Unit.

EASYGROW SYSTEMS
9 Hamilton Road, London W5 2EE. Exhibits: Rosum Easygrow Raised Flower-bed
System; Child's Adjustable Wheelchair.

FRASCARA, Jorge (1939, Argentina)
Professor of Painting and Teaching Methodology, Associate Head of Department of
Graphic Design, Escuela Panamericana de Arte, Venezuela 842, Buenos Aires.
Paper: The Role of a Graphic Design School in a Developing Country.

FRERIS, Leon (1934, Greece) BSc (Eng) MSc (Eng) PhD
Department of Electrical Engineering, Imperial College, South Kensington, London
SW7. Paper: Researches in Wind Power.

GERKEN, Peter Philip (1955, Gt Britain)
Department of Three-Dimensional Design, North Staffordshire Polytechnic, College
Road, Stoke-on-Trent. Exhibit: Emergency Fold-away Bath.

GRIFFITHS, Dot (1947, Gt Britain)
Imperial Sociology Unit, Imperial College, South Kensington, London SW7. Paper:
The Social Impact of Technology.

HAMNETT, Nicholas (1951, Gt Britain)
School of Industrial Design, Royal College of Art, London. Exhibit: Spinal Carriage
(with Nobuoki Ohtani).

HAWKES, Dennis (1939, Gt Britain)
Lecturer in the Department of Mechanical and Production Engineering, Polytechnic of
Wales, Pontypridd, Glamorgan. Paper: Design of equipment to extract methane and
fertiliser from organic waste (with Rex Horton).

HECHT, Hermann (1923, Germany) MSIA MSTD
Senior Lecturer and Course Director, Department of Graphic Design, Croydon College
of Design and Technology, Fairfield, Croydon, CR9 1DX. Paper: Assumptions in Design
Education (with Mauro Kunst).

HIGHLAND STONEWARE (SCOTLAND) LTD
Lochinver, Sutherland, Scotland. Exhibit: Highland Stoneware (Scotland) Ltd.

HINE, Marion (1952, Gt Britain) LSIA (toy design)
9 Weaver House, Pedley Street, London E1. Exhibit: Wooden Tactile Pendant Toys.

HORTON, Rex (1935, Gt Britain)
Senior Lecturer in Engineering Design, Department of Mechanical Engineering,
Polytechnic of Wales, Pontypridd, Glamorgan. Paper: Design of equipment to extract
methane and fertiliser from organic waste (with Dennis Hawkes).

HUGHES, Robert James (1950, Ireland)
109 Agincourt Avenue, Belfast. Exhibit: Rehabilitation and Environmental Improvement

INGRAM, Jack (1943, Gt Britain)
Senior Lecturer in Department of Three-Dimensional Design, Leeds Polytechnic,
Calverley Street, Leeds. Exhibit: Feeding System for an Athatoid Male.

JONES, J Christopher (1927, Gt Britain)
Aircraft Designer and Time Artist. 173 Walm Lane, London NW2. Paper: Thirty-five
Wishes.

JUPTNER, Heinrich (1932, Germany)
Professor of Ergonomics and Design Engineering at the Fachhochschule, Hannover,
Germany. Paper: Design for Need - the contribution of ergonomics. Exhibit: Design
by Ergonomics; for example, Safety in the Home.

KAN, Shiu Kay (1949, Hong Kong)
Architecture Department, Polytechnic of Central London, 309 Regent Street, London
W1R 8AL. Exhibits: Tin Can House (with Michael Potaliakhoff); Environmental
Education in Schools (with Jacqueline Sheehy).

KELLER, Goroslav (1946, Yugoslavia) MSc
Lecturer in Design and Product Development, Faculty for Foreign Trade, Zagreb
University, Lastovska 11, 4100 Zagreb, Yugoslavia. Paper: Environment-Tourism
Relationship - the problem of relationship between design and marketing.

KEMNITZER, Ronald B (1944, USA) MA
2276 Hulett Road, Okemos, Michigan 48864, USA. Exhibit: Toys for Hearing -
impaired children.

KHANNA, Sudarshan Kumar (1947, India)
National Institute of Design, Paldi Ahmedabad 380007, India. Paper: Design in the
Context of Rural Living in India.

KIRK, N S (1930, Gt Britain) MA PhD
Institute for Consumer Ergonomics, University of Technology, Loughborough, Leics,
LE11 3TU. Paper: The Design of an Urban Transport System using the Ergonomics
Approach.

KUNST, Mauro (1930, Brazil) MSIA
Architect. Lecturer in Department of Design, Croydon College of Design and
Technology, Fairfield, Croydon, CR9 1DX. Paper with Hermann Hecht.

LEWIS, James (1934, Gt Britain)
Architect. Disaster Research Unit, University of Bradford, Bradford, Yorks.
Paper: Pre-planning for Disasters.

LINDINGER, Herbert (1933, Austria)
Professor of Industrial Design, Technische Universität, Hannover, Germany. Exhibit:
Super 8 Film: planning of pedestrian streets and motor highway resting places.

LONDON COLLEGE OF FURNITURE
41-7 Commercial Road, London E1 1LA. Exhibit: Furniture for Handicapped Children.

LOVERING, Tim (1949, Gt Britain)
Industrial Design (Transport), Lanchester Polytechnic, Coventry. Exhibit: Invalid
Car (with Geoff Upex).

McLAREN, Ian (1940, Gt Britain) FSIA ITDG SIAD Alternative Design Group
Braunstein et McLaren associes, 5 Place des Reflets, 92400 Courbevoie, la Defense,
France. Exhibits: La Lorraine Aujourdhui; Pictograms for Public Authorities;
Signing - Metro de Lyon.

MACKEWN, Jennifer (1946, Gt Britain)
Friends of the Earth, 9 Poland Street, London W1. Paper: Materials Use, Re-use and
Recycling, and An Outline of FOE Recycling Schemes.

McQUISTON, Liz (1952, USA)
Department of Graphic Design, Royal College of Art, London. Editor of 'A Journal
from the Royal College of Art' and joint editor of Design for Need papers. Exhibit:

'So you're paralysed', a handbook for paralysed people and all who are involved in their care (design and illustration) - written by Bernadette Fallon.

McSWEENEY, Tony (1953, Gt Britain)
Department of Illustration, Royal College of Art, London. Exhibit: Using Gardens as Nature Reserves.

MALLEN, G L (1939, Gt Britain)
Cybernetician, Deputy Head of Research in the Department of Design Research, Royal College of Art, London. Paper: Shared Representations and Agreed Futures.

MARSH, R Brian (1947, Gt Britain)
Textile Research Unit, Royal College of Art, London. Exhibit: Decimal House.

MATTHIESSEN, Christine (1950, Gt Britain)
Department of Design Research, Royal College of Art, London. Exhibit: Home Care Equipment for the Elderly and Disabled.

MERCHANT, Arvind (1953, India)
Product Designer, National Institute of Design, Paldi, Ahmedabad 380007, India. Exhibit: Harvesting Implements (with Abir Mullick).

MOORE, Nick
Comtek, Weymouth Street, Snow Hill, Bath. Paper: Comtek: A Community Design Service.

MORGAN, Barry Patrick (1953, Gt Britain)
Graphic Design Department, Camberwell School of Art and Crafts, Peckham Road, London SE15. Exhibit: Age Action Year.

MORTON, Ian
Research Technician with the London Technical Group, 41 Queen's Gate, London SW7. Exhibit: Nutritional Assessment Equipment (with John Murlis).

MOSS, Carole
Department of Photography, Royal College of Art, London. Exhibit: The Royal Marsden Hospital Project (Photography).

MUGNAIONI, Paul (1951, Gt Britain)
Architect, University College, Gower Street, London WC1. Exhibit: A Strategy for Resettlement - Dagat Dagatan Squatter Relocation Project, Manila (with Mario Basso).

MULLICK, Abir (1954, India)
National Institute of Design, Paldi, Ahmedabad 380007, India. Exhibit: Harvesting Implements (with Arvind Merchant).

NASR, Ibrahim (1946, Sudan)
Edward Doherty & Sons (Sales) Ltd, Charlton Road, Edmonton. Exhibit: Child's Wheelchair.

NUTTALL, Mike (1949, Gt Britain) MDesRCA
113 Turnpike Lane, London N8. Exhibit: Lights (with John Stoddard).

OHTANI, Nobuoki (1948, Japan)
School of Industrial Design, Royal College of Art, London. Exhibit: Spinal Carriage
(with Nick Hamnett).

OLIVER, Rupert (1941, Gt Britain)
General freelance designer. 505 London Road, Croydon, Surrey. Exhibit: Totally
Soft Play Equipment.

ORNAMO
A working group of fashion designers. Unioninkatu 30, 00100 Helsinki 10, Finland.
Exhibit: Clothes and Toys for Handicapped Children.

PACKHAM, Michael John (1930, Gt Britain)
Flat 4, 20 Marine Square, Kemptown, Brighton BN2 1DN. Exhibit: Feeder Plate for
the Handicapped.

PIKE, Alexander (1924, Gt Britain) MA RIBA
Lecturer in Department of Architecture, University of Cambridge, Cambridge.
Paper: The Autarkic House: design objectives and strategies. Exhibit: 1:10 scale
model of proposed Autarkic House.

POTALIAKHOFF, Michael (1950, Gt Britain)
Polytechnic of Central London, 309 Regent Street, London W1R 8AL. Exhibit: Tin
Can House (with Shiu Kay Kan).

PYLE, D L (1940, Gt Britain)
Department of Chemical Engineering, Imperial College, South Kensington, London SW7.
Paper: Methane Generation; a Case Study in Engineering Education.

REES, Simon Griffith (1956, Gt Britain)
Department of Three-Dimensional Design, North Staffordshire Polytechnic, College
Road, Stoke-on-Trent ST4 2DE. Exhibit: Intensive Horticultural Growing System.

REEVE, Lynne (1946, Gt Britain)
School of Ceramics and Glass, Royal College of Art, London. Exhibit: Binary Testing
of Ceramic Glaze Materials (also described in Prof Queensberry's paper).

RUFF, Allan Richard (1940, Gt Britain) AMILA
Lecturer in Landscape at the Post-graduate Course in Landscape Design, Department
of Town and Country Planning, University of Manchester, Oxford Road, Manchester
M13 9PL. Paper: The Social Landscape.

RYALL, John (1945, Gt Britain) DipAD Lecturer at Newcastle School of Art and Design.
        Kate (1950, Gt Britain) DipAD ATC Designer.
Exhibit: Storyboard Language Teaching Aid.

SCOTT-HUNTER, Ian (1942, Gt Britain) BA
Senior Lectuer in Industrial Design, North Staffordshire Polytechnic, College Road,
Stoke-on-Trent. Paper: Community Playsites.

SEYMOUR, Richard William (1953, Gt Britain)
Department of Graphic Design, Royal College of Art, London. Exhibits: Drip Feed
Support, Medical Teaching Aid, Seeding System and Weighing System for Children.

SHEEHY, Jacqueline (1949, Gt Britain) BA(Soc)
Research Assistant in Recreation, Polytechnic of Central London, 309 Regent Street
London W1R 8AL. Exhibit: Environmental Education in Schools (with Shiu Kay Kan).

SOKOLOW, Anne(1941, USA) MA (UCLA) LSIA
Toy Designer. 183 The Vale, London NW11 8TL. Exhibits: Playmobile; House of
Sounds.

SOTAMAA, Yrjö (1942, Finland)
Head Instructor, Department of Interior Architecture and Furniture Design, University
of Industrial Art, Helsinki. Paper: Performance Criteria for Habilitation Environments
for Mentally Retarded Children. Exhibit: The Romping Room Project.

STEAD, Peter
c/o John Turner, 2A Woodsome Road, London NW5 1YR. Paper: Housing By People
(with John Turner).

STODDARD, John (1948, Gt Britain) MDesRCA
Industrial Designer. 113 Turnpike Lane, London N8. Exhibit: Lights (with Mike
Nuttall).

STRINGER, Guy
Deputy Director of Oxfam, 274 Banbury Road, Oxford. Paper: Waste Recycling in
Britain and the Oxfam Sanitation Project.

TONG, David Philip (1930, Gt Britain)
Development Manager, Kanga Hospital Products Ltd, PO Box 16, 345 Foleshill Road,
Coventry. Paper: Good Wine Needs No Bush, or the Need for Design. Exhibit: Kanga
Project.

TOVEY, Michael (1947, Gt Britain) MDesRCA
Lecturer in Industrial Design, Lanchester Polytechnic, Coventry. Exhibit: Mother and
Child Transport.

TURNER, John F C (1927, Gt Britain)
Lecturer at Architectural Association Graduate School and Development Planning Unit,
University College, London. Paper: Housing by People (with Peter Stead).

TYLER, Gerald (1943, Gt Britain) MDesRCA MSDI
Kilkenny Design Workshops, Kilkenny, Ireland. Exhibit: Plates and Cutlery for the
Disabled.

UPEX, Geoff (1952, Gt Britain)
School of Industrial Design, Royal College of Art, London. Exhibit: Invalid Car
(with Tim Lovering).

VALE, Robert and Brenda (1948 and 1949, Gt Britain)
The Horse and Gate, Witcham Toll, Sutton, Ely, Cambridgeshire. Paper: The
Autonomous House.

VICKERS, Peter (1947, Gt Britain) MDesRCA
Lecturer at Furniture Design Research Unit, Department of Three-Dimensional Design,
Trent Polytechnic, Burton Street, Nottingham, NG1 4BU. Exhibit: Mobiles Designed
for Waiting Room at Nottingham Children's Hospital (with Paul Briggs).

VIHMA, Susann (1946, Finland)
Teacher in the Department of Product and Environment Design, University of
Industrial Art, Helsinki. Paper: The Design of Work Environments and Equipment.
Exhibit: Clothing for the Chemical Industry.

WALLER, Diane Elizabeth (1943, Gt Britain)
Art Therapy Department, Goldsmiths College, Lewisham Way, New Cross SE14 6NQ.
Paper: The Effect of an Art Therapy Department on a Hospital Environment.

WEIGHTMAN, David (1947, Gt Britain) MDesRCA
68 Vernon Avenue, Rugby. Teacher of Industrial Design (Transport) at Lanchester
Polytechnic. Exhibits: Simple Motorised Vehicles; Pedal Driven Unit.

WHYATT, John (1947, Gt Britain) MDesRCA
17a Stoneleigh Street, London W11. Design for Need Assistant Exhibition Organiser.

WICKERT, Tony (1937, Austria)
Liberation Films, 6 Bramshill Gardens, London NW5. Paper: Portable Video at
Work - India and UK.

WILSON, Barry (1945, Gt Britain)
Researcher at Furniture Design Research Unit, Department of Three-Dimensional
Design, Trent Polytechnic, Burton Street, Nottingham NG1 4BU.

WILSON, Thomas (1953, Ireland)
11 Albert Street, Larne, Co Antrim, N Ireland. Exhibit: Civil Unrest and the
Communication System in Northern Ireland.

WOLFF, Heinz (1928, Germany) BSc
Head of Bioengineering Division, Clinical Research Centre, Watford Road, Harrow,
Middlesex. Paper: Data Presentation for Human Comprehension.

YORK UNIVERSITY DESIGN UNIT
King's Manor, York. Exhibit: Low-Energy Housing at Heslington, York.